Photographic Memory

PHOTOGRAPHIC MEMORY

✪

The Kennedy Assassination
November 22, 1963

RICHARD B. TRASK

Dallas, Texas
1996

ISBN 0-9648131-2-2

Published by
The Sixth Floor Museum
411 Elm Street
Dallas, Texas 75202-3301
214-653-6666

Dr. Marian Ann Montgomery, Project Coordinator
Gary Mack, Photographic Archivist
Teddy Diggs, Editor
Photographs of the cameras, except page 6, by Dean Bentley
Design and Production by Tom Dawson Graphic Design, Dallas, Texas
Printed by Authentic Press, Arlington, Texas
Film and Separations by CBS of Arlington, Arlington, Texas
Photographs on pages 6 and 13 courtesy of Richard Trask

This catalogue is adapted from the author's 640 page volume, *Pictures of the Pain: Photography and the assassination of President Kennedy*, published by Yeoman Press, 35 Centre Street, Danvers, MA 01923.

Frontispiece: Adpated from the photo on page 17.

TABLE OF CONTENTS

FOREWORD
vi

CATALOGUE

INTRODUCTION
1

ABRAHAM ZAPRUDER
5

JAMES ALTGENS
13

F. M. "MARK" BELL
20

CHARLES BRONSON
23

JACK DANIEL
30

MARY MOORMAN
33

ORVILLE NIX
39

PATSY PASCHALL
46

BERT SHIPP
49

JIM TOWNER
53

TINA TOWNER
53

PHIL WILLIS
59

CONCLUSION
65

FOREWORD

History has often been recorded by the first-hand observer. We rely on diaries, personal journals, notes and memoirs to "reconstruct" the historic event. In past centuries we have scrutinized these writings to understand—to create a "picture" of what took place.

Since the mid 1800s we've supplemented this written history with *photographic* history. Sometimes staged; sometimes recorded in the moment. There are literally hundreds of visual images which we mentally reference to "remember" an historic event—the Depression era woman cradling her hungry child, the sailor embracing a young lady in celebration of war's end, the astronaut planting the U.S. flag on lunar soil. We also include *moving* images in our mind's library—the Vietnam war, the Nixon resignation, the Challenger disaster, the Oklahoma City bombing.

These pictures are the building blocks we use to construct our personal vision of history. Many were made by professionals—some were made by amateurs. All combine to create a clarity and detail to the past never known before.

The Sixth Floor Museum's new exhibit of the Dealey Plaza cameras is tangible testimony to the importance of photography to our comprehension of the assassination. Here we have been able to preserve the real artifacts—cameras, photographs, as well as the personal stories of the photographers. Rememberers will be struck by the familiarity of a Bell & Howell home movie camera or an early Polaroid Highlander. Young people will be surprised by the cameras' antiquity when compared to today's contemporary minicams and automatics.

Some of the photographers cited were here on the job; others on a lark attempting to capture a presidential visit in a personal fashion. This exhibit commemorates their contribution to preserving our history.

Historian Richard Trask has done an outstanding job of summarizing the individual stories each camera and photographer preserved. His detailed research and historical perspective truly amplifies the new exhibit. For a more in-depth analysis of the images of the assassination I highly recommend Mr. Trask's full-length book *Pictures of the Pain.* He is the acknowledged expert of the photographic history and we are gratified that he has authored this exhibition catalog.

We must also acknowledge the hard work of the many people who worked together to conceive, research and assemble the exhibit. Dr. Marian Ann Montgomery led the team from initial concept to installation. She was ably assisted by Gary Mack, Bob Porter, Megan Bryant and the staff of Staples and Charles. We must also thank Steve Tilley, Jim Zeender, Sarah Bertalin, and Kitty Nicholson of the National Archives, Dean Bentley, James D. Wade for photographs of the cameras, Moses Olmos and Gary Blockley for timely assistance on the Altgens camera lens and Jim Baldwin for manuscript review. This catalog benefitted greatly from the editing of Teddy Diggs and the design of Tom Dawson.

Finally, we must acknowledge the photographers—James Altgens, Mark Bell, Charles Bronson, Jack Daniel, Mary Moorman, Orville Nix, Patsy Paschall, Bert Shipp, Jim and Tina Towner, Phil Willis and Abraham Zapruder—their sense of history truly allowed this exhibit to be assembled.

JEFF WEST
Executive Director
The Sixth Floor Museum

INTRODUCTION

We live in a world in which we are surrounded by photographic images. Much of what we know about our fellow man and the world in which we live comes to us through the medium of photography and its various branches. Picture books, newspapers, illustrated magazines, movie films, videotapes, and CD-ROMs saturate our lives. Much that we ourselves can never experience firsthand—the beauty of a distant galactic cluster as captured by the Hubble Space Telescope, or the intricacy of minute microorganisms as viewed by an electron microscope—can be revealed through photographs.

"I HAVE SEIZED THE LIGHT, I HAVE ARRESTED ITS FLIGHT!"
Louis Daguerre, 1839

Yet most of us take for granted this common means of visual preservation. Using cameras and videotape recorders, we create hundreds of snapshot photographs and moving pictures in which we capture both the mundane moments and the milestone highpoints of our lives. Our homes display framed pictures on walls and tables, while our drawers and closets brim with family images stored on old movie film, videocassettes, photographs, and slides. If we are fortunate, images of several generations of our family, many of whom we never personally knew, are treasured keepsakes. Photographs are such an important part of our lives and of our culture that remembered experiences of birthdays, vacations, backyard cookouts, hurricanes, and snowstorms are often recollected not from our mind's eye but rather from the images shown in our pictures.

This visual melange that so permeates our lives is of recent date in terms of human history. In 1839 the Frenchman Louis Daguerre was the first to create a successful photographic system for general use. By means of a polished silver-coated copper sheet, a dark box, a simple lens, and various chemicals, Daguerre could entrap light and capture a fleeting, ephemeral image of reality upon the shiny plate. Remarking on his process, Daguerre exclaimed, "I have seized the light, I have arrested its flight!" From those simple yet revolutionary beginnings, we now can create, preserve, examine, and cherish any image in which light interplays with matter.

Yet there are—and have always been—limits to what and how much of reality can be photographed. These limits are both cultural and technological and are also

Opposite page: Adapted from the Willis photo on page 61.

dependent on the competence of the photographer. In the mid-nineteenth century, photographic plates were singular objects holding a view that was a mirror image of reality, where left and right were reversed, and no independent negative was generated. In addition, the photographic process required enough time to allow light to impress itself onto the plate. Thus the creation of daguerreotypes, ambrotypes, and ferrotypes necessitated that the subject remain in a stiff pose for several minutes. Few exterior views and virtually no scenes exhibiting movement could be successfully photographed. Though thousands of soldiers' portraits were created during the American Civil War in 1861–65, as well as staged encampment scenes and still-life aftermaths of battles, no views survive of a battle in progress or of a truly candid event.

The introduction of gelatin dry-plates, followed later by negative film on plastic stock, allowed for multiple copies of original scenes. Likewise, faster film emulsions and improved cameras and lenses meant ever shorter exposure time, which in turn permitted capturing more detail and freezing motion. In 1889 Kodak revolutionized picture-taking by introducing a truly simple amateur system whereby a box camera was preloaded with film; the photographer needed only to point and shoot. After the entire camera was returned to Kodak, the company would do the rest, sending back photographic prints mounted on card stock.

Thomas Alva Edison's inventive genius is credited with developing, in the late 1880s, the first practical motion-picture camera able to produce numerous images taken at split-second increments. When the long film strips were projected through a light source and a coordinated shutter system, the image appeared to move, as in real life.

By the beginning of the twentieth century, photography was no longer the sole domain of technically sophisticated professionals and serious amateurs; it was now a relatively inexpensive pastime for millions of people. The camera introduced a democratization of artistic expression and offered the possibility of capturing the mundane as well as the exceptional subject in life.

By the 1930s, photographic images, as captured by professional cameramen and photographers and as displayed to the public in movie newsreels, newspapers, or illustrated magazines, had become an integral part of life. Now-famous images became an indelible part of America's shared remembrance of historic events: a soldier caught as he was felled by a bullet during the Spanish Civil War; the horrific, fiery explosion of the dirigible *Hindenburg;* Jesse Owens winning a race during the 1936 Berlin Olympic games; the battleship *Arizona* taking a decimating direct hit at Pearl Harbor; the raising of the American flag on top of Mount Suribachi, Iwo Jima; and President Harry Truman happily displaying the erroneous newspaper headline "Dewey Defeats Truman."

Historical photography is typically defined as the use of photographic images to facilitate the study and interpretation of history. The use of photography as historical evidence is limited, however. Photography may exhibit partial truths, personal biases, and distortions of reality, and it can never tell the whole story of an event. In examining photographs as historical documents, one must cautiously realize these limits. The medium upon which a photographic image is made skews our view of the event being photographed, whether caused by the inferior optics of a cheap box camera or the tonal differences among present-day color film dyes. Thus we must critically examine visual images, understanding that the photographer can distort, simplify, or misrepresent reality by including or excluding items (purposefully or accidentally) or by pointing the camera in one direction to the exclusion of others. Yet for all the potential shortcomings, photography comes closer than does any other paper document or record to being a true trace of reality.

Though millions of average Americans have owned and operated cameras during most of the twentieth century, the photographic recording of major news stories was almost always the domain of professional photojournalists. One of the first major news events to break the mold was the assassination of President John F. Kennedy. In the Dallas, Texas, motorcade on November 22, 1963, most of the camera professionals assigned to cover the president's activities were in cars many lengths behind the president's Lincoln convertible. Thus the recording of this seminal event in American history became the unwitting responsibility of local amateurs, who were taking pictures of the motorcade not as artifacts for the historic record but rather as souvenir keepsakes of a president's visit to their community.

Almost everyone knows of Abraham Zapruder's assassination film, but few realize that about three dozen people had cameras with them in the Dealey Plaza area of Dallas on that mild fall day at noontime. These incidental observers of history recorded, in a variety of photographic formats and with differing equipment and skills, the last moments in the life of a president of the United States. These photographers captured on their film—in a form truer than any person's eye or memory—brief, relevant, and dramatic slices of the reality of the scene. As a result of their camera work, they created images that can be examined and interpreted as true historical artifacts of the incident itself.

Several of these pictures gained wide publication and notoriety and were the subject of later controversy and scientific study. The U.S. government reviewed many of these photographic images when it sought to determine the source of the fatal shots. Due to the speed and complexity of the investigations, however, some of the cameras and images were never included in any government inquiry.

The people of America also used these images, to help them understand how

President Kennedy died and to ascertain the validity of the Warren Commission's conclusion that all the shots came from the sixth floor of the Texas School Book Depository building. And researchers have analyzed the pictures over the years to determine if there was a shooter in another location. Over time, many other photos and films have come to light, and more modern technology has been used to enhance the images taken on November 22, 1963, in order to discover what was actually recorded. The history of these photos and films, and of the people and cameras that created them, makes an intriguing story.

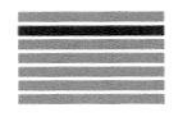

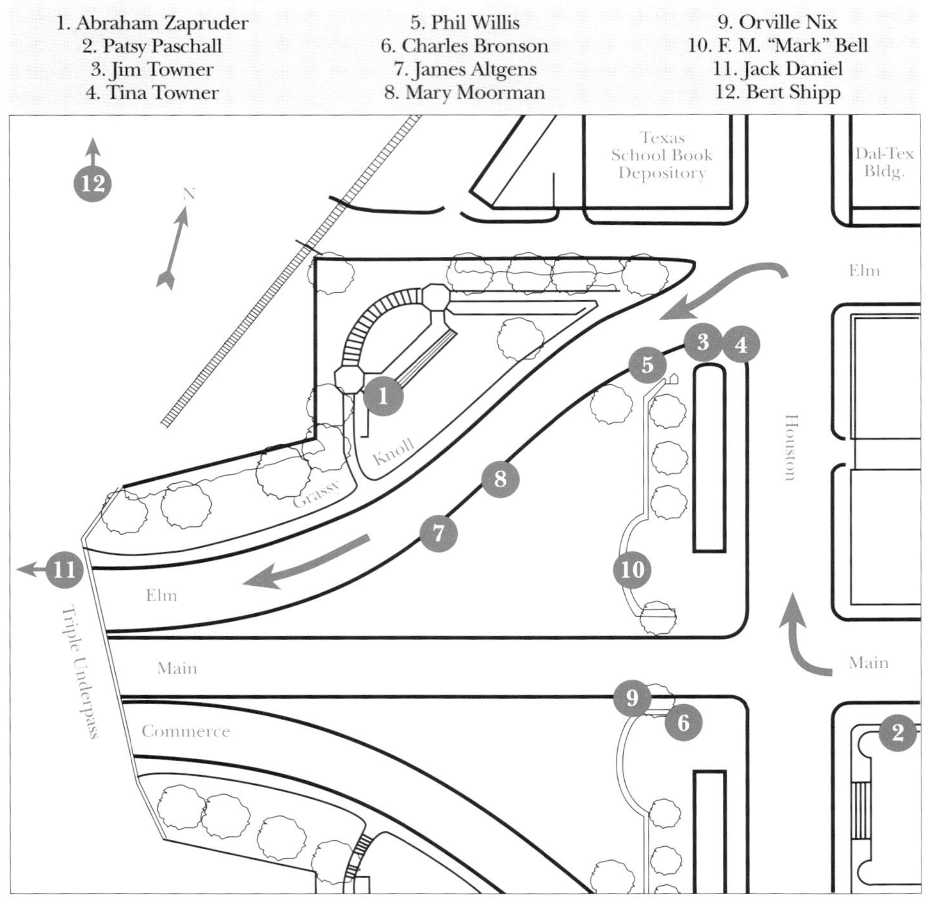

Map showing Dealey Plaza photographer locations at the moment these historic pictures were taken. Willis, Altgens, Nix, and Bell took additional pictures at one or more other locations. *Map design courtesy R. B. Cutler. Research by Gary Mack*

ABRAHAM ZAPRUDER

Abraham Zapruder, right, describing the fatal head wound on local television about ninety minutes after the assassination. *Courtesy WFAA-TV.*

Abraham Zapruder was born in czarist Russia in 1905. Of Jewish ancestry, Zapruder emigrated to the United States in 1920, moving to Dallas, Texas, in 1941. An affable man, Zapruder in 1949 went into business for himself and created Jennifer Juniors, Inc., which manufactured a line of women's clothing. By 1963 the company was located in the Dal-Tex building, at 501 Elm Street on the northeast corner of Elm and Houston Streets.

To chronicle his family's growth, in 1962 Zapruder had purchased a top-of-the-line 8mm movie camera from Peacock Jewelry Company on Elm Street. The Model 414PD Bell & Howell Zoomatic Director Series camera, which retailed for about $200, included a Varamat 9mm to 27mm f1.8 lens and a leather carrying case. The camera, serial number AS13486, featured a built-in electric eye, a spring-wind indicator, and adjustable shutter speeds for animation (single-frame), run (regular-speed, 18 frames per second), and slow-motion (48 frames per second) filming. The December 1963 *Consumer Reports* buying guide rated this model as the best of the zoom-lens cameras that were tested. The magazine noted the camera's optical performance at the normal and the wide-angle modes as "very good" and at tele-

This Bell & Howell 414PD Zoomatic Director Series is the only camera used to film the entire assassination. Without the film taken by Abraham Zapruder, we would know few details of the actual shooting. Since the effect of only one gun shot is obvious, speculation remains about when others were fired. Zapruder gave the camera to the Bell & Howell Corporation, which donated it to the National Archives in 1966. *Loaned courtesy of the National Archives.*

photo as "excellent." The convenience, versatility, and speed consistency of the camera were also rated "excellent," far better than any other tested zoom-lens or turret model. In late November 1963, Zapruder's camera was loaded with Kodachrome II color safety film.

Most people in the Dal-Tex building knew that on Friday, November 22, President Kennedy would be visiting Dallas. A lunchtime motorcade would take the presidential party right by the building on the way to a luncheon program at the Dallas Trade Mart. Zapruder initially talked about bringing his camera to work on Friday to film the event. November 22 dawned overcast, however, and Zapruder left the camera at home. As the morning wore on, the clouds lifted, leaving behind a sparkling Texas autumn day. Zapruder's secretary, Lillian Rogers, urged him to go home and get his camera, since a president of the United States did not ride by the office every day. Relenting to his secretary's good-natured badgering, Zapruder made the fourteen-mile round-trip to his home and back.

At around noon, Zapruder walked the short distance to the Dealey Plaza park area. Looking about the plaza, he noticed a rectangular block some four feet high at the western end of the decorative concrete pergola area. This location would afford him an elevated perch, giving him a sweeping view of Elm Street. After somewhat clumsily groping up onto the pedestal, Zapruder asked his receptionist, Marilyn Sitzman, who was nearby, to stand behind him so that if he got dizzy, she could hold onto him.

The complete Elm Street motorcade sequence that Zapruder filmed runs about 26 seconds. The 486 frames, all subsequently assigned individual numbers for investigative reference, had been exposed through Zapruder's telephoto camera lens at an average of 18⅓ frames per second. The first 132 frames shot were of the lead motorcycle escort. When Zapruder started his camera again for an approximately 19-second uninterrupted run, his first frame showed the presidential Lincoln already on Elm Street, having completed its Houston Street turn.

Bell & Howell marketed its cameras in department store newspaper ads. This ad, showing the same model camera Zapruder used, coincidentally appeared in a Los Angeles newspaper two days after the assassination.
Travis E. Brickett Collection/The Sixth Floor Museum

The custom-built 1961 presidential Lincoln Continental drop-top convertible sedan was equipped with removable, transparent-plastic roof panels. These so-called bubble-top attachments had been removed for the Dallas motorcade. The motorcade, consisting of about twenty-three vehicles as well as escort motorcycles, was scheduled to wind its way from Love Field in Dallas through the downtown business district and on to the Dallas Trade Mart, where the president was to give an address. Those riding in the president's car included Secret Service agent and driver William Greer and Assistant Special Agent-in-Charge Roy Kellerman in the front seat. Texas Governor John B. Connally and his wife, Nellie, were in the right and left jump seats, while President and Mrs. Kennedy were in the

Frame 225, shortly after the first or second shot, shows that Kennedy has been wounded.

rear seat, with the president on the right side. Four Dallas police motorcycles flanked the car's rear bumper, closely followed by a 1956 Cadillac touring sedan known as the "follow-up" car and occupied by eight Secret Service agents and two presidential aides. The bulk of the motorcade, carrying the vice-president, dignitaries, staff, and press, followed behind.

In later testimony before the Warren Commission, which President Lyndon B. Johnson created after the assassination to determine the facts of the case, Zapruder described what he recalled witnessing as the presidential Lincoln came into his view on Elm Street. "I heard the first shot and I saw the President lean over and grab himself like this [holding his left chest area] . . . for a moment I thought it was, you know, like you say, 'Oh, he got me,' when you hear a shot. You've heard these expressions. And then I saw—I don't believe the President is going to make jokes like this, but before I had a chance to organize my mind, I heard a second shot and then I saw his head open up and the blood and everything came out and I started—I can hardly talk about it." Recalling the horror of the scene he had filmed, Zapruder began to cry. Pausing briefly to compose himself, the businessman then continued his recollection. "Then I started yelling, 'They killed him, they killed him,' and I just felt that somebody had ganged up on him and I was still shooting the pictures until he got under the underpass—I don't even know how I did it."

"... I WAS STILL SHOOTING THE PICTURES UNTIL HE GOT UNDER THE UNDERPASS—I DON'T EVEN KNOW HOW I DID IT."
Abraham Zapruder

To call Zapruder's film remarkable is an exaggerated understatement. It is, due to the subject matter and the clear angle of view, undoubtedly one of the most important films ever made. As far as is known, it is the only complete film of the assassination. We watch as the president and the governor react to being shot, followed by a short sequence in which Mrs. Kennedy leans toward and holds the arm of the president. The next is a terrible scene as the president's head explodes. Like a rag doll, he crumples into his seat while his wife scurries out toward the car trunk. To those who view this film, it is a moment of gruesome reality, even though experienced only through the sense of sight, a sense that is further restricted by a narrow angle of view and by the technological shortcomings of the 8mm film size. This amateur home movie, almost not even made, would soon become one of the best-known artifacts of the twentieth century.

Frame 312, shown in close up, corresponds to the moment the fatal head shot was fired.

Yet inherent in the very existence of this film is the important caveat that although we see what the camera recorded, understanding what we see is open to much subjective interpretation. Though this strip of film shows us, in excruciating detail, the fact that a president died, it also opens up to immense speculation the exact means of his death. Had the Zapruder film never been made, or had it been lost to us, much of the later debate over the actual sequence of the shots, the timing of the shots, and the victims' reactions to the shots would not have taken place. Ironically, many of these later controversies surrounding the facts of the assassination found birth in the very piece of evidence that brought us the most truthful visual record of the assassination itself. Watching the film, we all become spectators who ponder the various possible meanings of the preserved images. As a result of this film, various government agencies and a subculture of assassination investigators have delved into science and pseudo-science—studying physics, ballistics, medicine, pathology, human reaction to stimuli, and photo interpretation—all to find the truth.

THOUGH THIS STRIP OF FILM SHOWS US, IN EXCRUCIATING DETAIL, THE FACT THAT A PRESIDENT DIED, IT ALSO OPENS UP TO IMMENSE SPECULATION THE EXACT MEANS OF HIS DEATH.

Without Zapruder's film, we might have had simpler, though not necessarily truer, answers than we now have, answers that might have simplified the investigative process and resulted in less trauma for our national psyche in the intervening years. But Zapruder was there, and his 26½ seconds of film, though unavailable to the public for years, could not remain unseen forever, nor could the film be ignored by those who needed to know the truth or at least part of the truth of how the event occurred.

During the afternoon of November 22, 1963, Zapruder had his film developed, then made three first-generation copies. Later that day Forrest Sorrels, the Dallas Secret Service field office agent-in-charge, went to Zapruder's office and was given custody of two of the copies of the film; he assured Zapruder that they would be for official use only. These prints were subsequently used by the FBI and the Secret Service in the government's investigation.

The existence and potential newsworthiness of this film soon became known to many in the media. *LIFE* magazine editor Richard B. Stolley arrived in Dallas by the end of the day. *LIFE* had a reputation as the premier weekly illustrated magazine, one that prided itself on its ability to snag and illustrate important stories. Stolley contacted Zapruder and was able—through good timing, *LIFE*'s deep money pockets, and the magazine's fine reputation as perceived by Zapruder—to acquire all reproduction rights and the original Zapruder assassination film for the undisclosed (at the time) sum of $150,000.

LIFE published a selection of film frames in its November 29, 1963, issue. The emotional impact on the American public was immense. Though additional frames would be reproduced in subsequent issues of *LIFE* over the next few years, and though several sample frames were made available to the media for limited distribution, the dogged refusal by Time-LIFE, the corporation that owned *LIFE* magazine, to allow this key historical record and evidence of the assassination to be viewed by the public in any form other than what *LIFE* believed to be appropriate was the cause for legitimate criticism. This possessive and secretive attitude would help foster the belief that *LIFE,* consciously or not, was significantly responsible for preventing serious nongovernmental investigators from learning the entire truth about the assassination.

If the Zapruder film had significance as a historical artifact, what about the camera that created the film? In early December, Zapruder loaned the camera to the government. The FBI had realized that a key fact in understanding the time frame of the assassination was gaining a firm knowledge of the speed of the camera itself. Following a series of clock tests, the FBI lab reported, "This camera when operated at normal 'run' speed operates at 18⅓ frames per second."

Meanwhile Bell & Howell had made an agreement with Zapruder to exchange his camera for a newer model, the original being an appropriate addition to the company's archival collection. After the Warren Commission's use of the camera in field study tests in Dallas in May 1964, tests conducted under the auspices of the FBI and the Secret Service, the camera was given to Bell & Howell. Two years later, in December 1966, Bell & Howell donated the original Zapruder camera and its carrying case to the U.S. government.

The Warren Commission relied heavily on in-house studies of what the Zapruder film revealed. Its *Hearings* volumes, made available to the public in November 1964, included black and white reproductions of over 160 frames from the film. As a result, for the first time, interested researchers had a chance to examine for themselves much of the film. This was followed in 1969, as an indirect result of the Garrison investigation, by the circulation of bootleg copies of the movie and by the first television broadcast of the film in March 1975. The film became more widely available, and criticism of Time-LIFE's restrictive policy made the company so uncomfortable that in April 1975 the film's ownership was transferred back to the Zapruder family for one dollar. Zapruder himself lived in Dallas until his death in 1970. He avoided seeing his film and told people of his occasional nightmares of reliving the horror of the assassination.

Numerous theories, lectures, and books have been produced as a result of the study of Zapruder's film. The Zapruder film remains one of the key pieces of his-

> "Depending on your point of view, it proves almost anything you want it to prove."
>
> *Richard Stolley, "LIFE" magazine*

toric evidence in the assassination of President Kennedy. It has been seen by millions and studied by hundreds of people over the years. Various government agencies, major corporations, and institutions of higher learning have been caught up in the interpretation of this film's meaning, while scores of objective and subjective amateur sleuths have attempted to exact from it elusive truths. It is perhaps the best evidence of what happened to the president, but even as the best evidence, it falls far short of enabling us to comprehend exactly how the president was killed and by whom. As Richard Stolley, the journalist who captured the movie sequence for *LIFE* magazine, once commented about this film clip, "Depending on your point of view, it proves almost anything you want it to prove." The film, though compelling, is truly grotesque, and like Abraham Zapruder, many who see it have trouble getting the vision of horror out of their minds or their dreams, for it indeed captured one of our worst national nightmares.

JAMES ALTGENS

James Altgens, as he appeared in 1963.

Of the many photographers, both amateur and professional, who would take pictures of the events before, during, and after the few seconds of gunshots that would sidetrack the course of American history, no one was at the scene with more premeditated camera planning than James Altgens, a man not originally even scheduled to be viewing the parade.

James William "Ike" Altgens was, except for his service during World War II, a lifelong resident of Dallas, having been born there on April 28, 1919. Orphaned as a child, Altgens was reared by a widowed aunt. In 1938, at the age of nineteen, he began his long career with the Associated Press (AP). In 1945, after his return to Dallas from Coast Guard service and his marriage to Clara B. Halliburton, Altgens began making photographs for the Associated Press News Bureau.

By the 1960s, Altgens, a genial Texan with a deep melodic voice, was serving the Dallas Bureau of the Associated Press as a wirephoto operator, though often functioning also as a photographer. He had photographed John F. Kennedy once before when, in November 1961, the new president had gone to Bonham, Texas, to attend the funeral of Speaker of the House of Representatives Sam Rayburn.

Years later Altgens recalled how he came to be at the scene of the president's assassination in 1963. "While I was originally assigned to work as photo editor on November 22, I urged the assignment editor and bureau chief to let me go down to the triple underpass to make a scenic view of the presidential caravan with the Dallas skyline in the background." This area had no scheduled photographic coverage, and Altgens' persistence got him the assignment.

> "THIS MEANT THAT WHAT I TOOK I HAD TO MAKE SURE IT WAS GOOD— I DIDN'T HAVE TIME FOR SECOND CHANCES."
> *James Altgens*

Wanting to be in position in plenty of time to take photos of the motorcade, Altgens walked over to the triple underpass, where Main, Elm, and Commerce Streets travel under the railroad tracks, at about 11:15 A.M. Altgens brought with him his personal 35mm Nikkorex-F single-lens reflex camera. He had purchased the camera mounted with a 50mm lens in January 1963 from Medo Photo Supply Corporation of New York, through the Associated Press. It cost $157 and was marked with serial number 371734. On November 22 the camera body was mounted with a 105mm telephoto lens and loaded with Eastman Kodak Tri-X pan film. On major assignments, photographers were usually given motor-driven cameras, but since Altgens had not been originally assigned as a photographer, he took his own hand-cocked camera, which did not lend itself to speed shooting. As Altgens explained, "This meant that what I took I had to make sure it was good—I didn't have time for second chances."

Two uniformed police officers were stationed on top of the underpass. One

As the only professional to capture the assassination on film, Associated Press photographer James Altgens used this Nikkorex-F to make his pictures, the first to appear on television and in newspapers. *Camera courtesy James Altgens. Lens gift of Gary Blockley*

came over and challenged Altgens, asking if he was a railroad employee. Altgens said no, showed him his press tag, and explained that he was assigned to take some photographs of the motorcade. His explanation did not help. The officer was adamant that the area was private property and that no one but railroad personnel was permitted in the area. Altgens decided not to press the issue and moved on to find another spot. He walked over to the corner of Houston and Main Streets. This seasoned photographer could see potential photo opportunities here, since the motorcade would be traveling down the sloping grade from upper Main Street toward his position. This view might make for a usable shot of the motorcade in the middle of a large Dallas crowd, with the tall buildings giving a cavernous mood to the picture. Altgens saw that after taking a few pictures here, he could then run across Dealey Plaza and again catch the motorcade on Elm Street as it proceeded toward the triple underpass.

Altgens took his first two shots of the procession as it traveled toward him. He waited to make his first exposure just at the point when the president's car hit a sunlit break between the shadows of the buildings. Readjusting his focus, he waited for a clear close-up view of the presidential limousine. As the shining blue-black Lincoln swung around the corner, both Governor and Mrs. Connally were looking toward Altgens' side of the street. The president was also looking toward the camera and raising his right forearm in a wave. Altgens remembered, "Jackie Kennedy was looking at me, but the wind had just gotten up catching the First Lady's hat." She instinctively reached to hold it with her white-gloved left hand, obscuring her face to Altgens' lens. Though Mrs. Kennedy's face was not in the picture that Altgens took, the others were, as were also the features of more than twenty smiling spectators across the street on the northeast corner of Houston and Main, all captured on the film in a frozen moment of time and light. This photo by Altgens would be published in hundreds of newspapers across the country within the next six hours, with the caption to the photograph alluding to the last few moments of happiness before the horror.

This photo by Altgens would be published in hundreds of newspapers across the country within the next six hours, with the caption to the photograph alluding to the last few moments of happiness before the horror.

Cocking his camera, Altgens took an additional photograph as the president's car and the Secret Service follow-up vehicle moved away from him. Altgens then sprinted down the sloping grade over the grassed infield area of the plaza. He reached the curb of the south side of Elm Street, about 240 feet from the intersection of Elm and Houston Streets, at the time the motorcade was making a sharp left-hand turn onto Elm.

Altgens had the camera's aperture at f11 with a shutter speed of 1/1000 of a second. Stepping off the curb into the street, Altgens looked into his viewfinder, and just a fraction ahead of his clicking the shutter, he heard a noise that sounded like a firecracker going off somewhere from behind the approaching car. The noise was extraneous to Altgens and held no significance for his task. Spot news photographers don't typically have the benefit of time to study their subject, since things happen so quickly around them. As Altgens vividly described years later: "My first instinct was 'well, they're shooting firecrackers up there,' or some kind of celebration on behalf of the President. And then I hear [*sic*] it again as the car comes on down. No one had the foggiest idea that something was taking place." His developed picture, however, showed in detail what eyes and mind could not so quickly comprehend.

Portions of the first two stories of the front side of the Texas School Book Depository are in view, with at least four persons watching the procession from the front entrance. While the spectators seem oblivious to anything wrong, the occupants of the president's car have had their attention diverted from these friendly onlookers. The governor has turned sharply to his right and seems to be wincing. The eyes and nose of President Kennedy are obscured by the limousine's rear-view mirror, but his lips appear pursed and he is cocked slightly to the left with his left arm horizontal to the plane of his mouth. His fingers are clenched. The white-gloved right hand of Mrs. Kennedy is cradling his arm. Motorcycle officer James Chaney, on the left side of the picture, has turned his head sharply to his left, while the other two visible motorcycle men seem to be looking toward the limousine.

In the Secret Service follow-up car, driver Samuel Kinney, Agent-in-Charge Emory Roberts, agent Clint Hill on the driver's forward running-board position, and presidential assistant Dave Powers, his forehead obscured by the rear-view mirror, seem to be looking directly at the president. The Altgens picture captures the scene just a few seconds into the assassination of the president when, except for the victims themselves, few had had time to react to the intrusive noise they had just heard.

Still in the midst of taking his pictures and oblivious to the danger around him, Altgens stepped back onto the curb. He quickly wound his film to the next frame, adjusted his focus to 15 feet, and raised the Nikkorex to eye level, wanting to get a good close-up of the president and Mrs. Kennedy. As the limousine passed just about 15 feet to the front of him and as he was about ready to snap the picture, Altgens heard another report. A high-velocity bullet struck the president's head. "Fragments of his head fell right at my feet. That was some heck of an explosion when it hit his head. His skull just disintegrated and bone and flesh flying." The hor-

Altgens' third Dealey Plaza photograph corresponds to Zapruder frame 255, about midway through the assassination. *Courtesy AP/Wide World Photos.*

ror was unexpected; Kennedy's head was covered with blood. According to Altgens, "It stunned me so at what I saw, that I failed to do my duty and make the picture that I was trying to make." Altgens heard Mrs. Kennedy cry "oh, no!" as the president's body slumped over into her lap, and she moved toward the car's trunk.

"The horror was unexpected . . ."
James Altgens

The photographer's shock at such a ghastly sight was momentary, and the veteran's instinct took hold. Altgens stepped out to the curb and aimed his camera at the now quickly accelerating presidential vehicle. He shot a forlorn scene in which agent Clint Hill is on the limousine's rear step. Mrs. Kennedy is moving from the trunk back into the car. The white lead car is a few lengths ahead, just starting into the shadow of the railroad overpass, on top of which some ten spectators can be seen peering down at the horror below.

With the presidential Lincoln disappearing beneath the underpass, Altgens made a picture of the activity across Elm Street, showing amateur moviemaker

Abraham Zapruder and his secretary, Marilyn Sitzman, just after they had gotten down from the concrete block from where Zapruder had filmed the assassination. Altgens quickly crossed the street. The area was in "utter confusion" as uniformed policemen went racing up the incline of the grassy knoll. Altgens said of the scene: "Well, I thought they were onto something. I was satisfied that the shot came from the rear, but I didn't know where in the rear. So I figured they had spotted the guy somewhere and they had chased him up here, and I wanted to come over and get a picture of the guy—if they had such a person in custody. And I came over here and by the time I can get up to the hill, they're turned around and are coming back. And they hadn't found anything."

"She cried 'Oh, No!' The motorcade sped on."

Bob Johnson Jr., AP Bureau Chief

Realizing the importance of what he had seen and the pictures he had taken, Altgens sprinted back to the Dallas Morning News building. Arriving at the third-floor AP wirephoto office, Altgens blurted out to Bureau Chief Bob Johnson Jr., "The President has been shot!" Johnson yelled "bulletin!" as he typed the most important lines of his career. At 12:39 Central Standard Time the bulletin was on the wire. "Dallas, Nov. 22 (AP)—President Kennedy was shot today just as his motorcade left downtown Dallas. Mrs. Kennedy jumped up and grabbed Mr. Kennedy. She cried 'Oh, No!' The motorcade sped on."

Altgens remembered what happened while the bulletin was being readied: "Someone grabbed my camera, removed the film and took it in to process it, because they wanted me on the telephone reporting what I saw. We did an extraordinary good job, because within twenty minutes of the assassination we had a picture rolling on the wire." The photo caption of the motorcade under fire, one of three of Altgens' photos sent out on the wirephoto network, read: "(DN2) DALLAS, TEX., NOV. 22—KENNEDY SHOT IN DALLAS—President John F. Kennedy was shot today just as his motorcade left downtown Dallas. He was taken to Parkland Hospital. Secret Service men are looking from where the shots came from (AP Wirephoto) (cel61303 stf—jwa) 1963." Although the published photographs that were circulated all over the nation and the world clearly showed that an AP photographer was present at the assassination, for months no government official contacted Altgens or the Dallas AP office about the events the photographer had witnessed.

Several members of the news media spotted the uncanny resemblance of accused assassin Lee Harvey Oswald to one of the men standing in the doorway of the Book Depository building, peering out at the motorcade in Altgens' fifth photo. If this man was Oswald, how could he be accused of doing the shooting?

The FBI was busy checking out this identity question. On November 25, agents interviewed Roy S. Truly, manager of the Book Depository, who identified the person in the doorway as employee Billy Nolan Lovelady. They also spoke to Lovelady, who confirmed that he was indeed the person in the picture and who admitted that there was a resemblance between Oswald and himself. Lovelady later told an interviewer what happened when the agents showed him the Altgens picture: "Right away I pointed to me and they seemed relieved. One had a big smile on his face because it wasn't Oswald. They said they had a big discussion down at the FBI and one guy said it just had to be Oswald." On January 30, 1964, Assistant Manager William H. Shelley was also interviewed. He stated that the person in the photo was Lovelady and that he, Shelley, had been standing next to Lovelady that day.

Although critics of the 1964 Warren Commission investigation continued for years to question the identity of the man at the Book Depository entrance, spurred on by a mixup of what shirt Lovelady was wearing that day, the evidence is quite overwhelming that the person was in fact Lovelady. This conclusion was strengthened as a result of the work in 1978 of the House Select Committee on Assassinations.

On July 22, 1964, Wesley Liebeler, assistant counsel for the Warren Commission, took testimony from Altgens in Dallas. Liebeler centered the questioning on the manner in which Altgens had taken his photographs, his movement in the plaza, the number, spacing, and direction of the gunshots, his distance from the limousine, and his ability to identify anyone in his fifth photograph. Until the news stories about their negligence surfaced, the federal investigative bodies made no effort to contact Altgens. Instead of actively seeking out this man who had been an important witness to the killing, the government had to be prodded into action by newspaper questions.

Until the news stories about their negligence surfaced, the federal investigative bodies made no effort to contact Altgens.

Retired from the Associated Press in 1979, Altgens was often sought out by assassination buffs for his recollections. He did not suffer gladly the eyewitnesses to November 22, 1963, who changed and embellished their stories over the years. He was bemused and perplexed by many of the conspiracy theorists who spent much of their time devising intricate scenarios and who attempted to convince him, with detailed diagrams and rambling letters, that what he had seen and experienced was incorrect and that what they imagined was the truth. He told one friend, "Until those people come up with solid evidence to support their claims, I see no value in wasting my time with them." Both Altgens and his wife died at their Dallas home in December 1995.

F. M. "MARK" BELL

F. M. "Mark" Bell, at his home in the Oak Cliff area of Dallas in about 1963. *Courtesy F. M. Bell.*

F. M. "Mark" Bell was a native of Limestone County, Texas. Born in 1918, Bell had seen combat in the 1st Marine Division during the Second World War. A letter carrier for the U.S. Postal Department, he prepared his daily deliveries at the Post Office Terminal Annex building and then delivered them on a walking route that took him into the nearby downtown commercial area.

Bell owned a simple, one-lens Brownie 8 movie camera. On November 22, Bell's sixteen-year-old daughter wanted to be excused from school so that she could see the downtown presidential motorcade. Since Bell didn't want his daughter to miss school, he agreed to take a movie of the parade so that she could see it later. Thus a historic piece of film was created by a strict but sympathetic father.

Bell recalled his chosen position to view the motorcade: "I was on the northwest corner of Main and Houston. There were people around taking pictures. I was standing up on a pillar that was made for aesthetic purposes, I suppose, and I was standing on top of that. It was about four feet tall." Bell initially took a few seconds of film to record the view up Main Street toward the direction of the anticipated procession.

Bell watched as the presidential vehicle traveled down Main Street; he filmed some 15½ seconds of the scene, picking up the view again as the car moved up Houston Street, then again after it turned onto Elm Street, and passed the front door of the Texas School Book Depository. About 62 frames were taken of this Elm Street sequence, until Bell's view was obscured by a tree. "I jumped down from the thing that I was on and ran around to the end of it so that I could get a better picture. That's when the shots were fired, while I was down."

Bell recollected hearing three shots, two of which were "bunched," but he could not recall which ones. Just after the shots had been fired and he had reached the end of the peristyle, Bell immediately began filming. "The President's car took off like a bat out of Hades, and I got a shot of it going under the underpass—so you know something had happened. A motorcycle was lying down where a cop was behind it trying to see what was going on. People were running in all directions. You knew something was happening, but had no way of knowing what. I just kept shooting pictures."

"THE PRESIDENT'S CAR TOOK OFF LIKE A BAT OUT OF HADES, AND I GOT A SHOT OF IT GOING UNDER THE UNDERPASS . . ."

F.M. "Mark" Bell

Bell's film captured this action in three erratic but dramatic sequences. The first sequence included the motorcade lead car being overtaken at the underpass

Never questioned by the Warren Commission, F. M. "Mark" Bell used this Kodak Brownie 8 to film the Kennedy limousine on Houston Street and just after it turned onto Elm. After the shooting, Bell changed positions and filmed the limousine entering the triple underpass. *Loaned courtesy of F.M. Bell.*

About one minute after the assassination, witnesses running up the grassy knoll into the parking lot in search of a gunman. Bell was the only amateur to film the event. *Courtesy F. M. Bell.*

by the president's car. The follow-up car, the vice-president's convertible, and the sedan escort followed close behind. He then captured the activity around the grassy knoll. The motorcade camera cars traveled down Elm Street while more and more spectators arrived in the area, crossing the street and running up the knoll to the area around, adjacent to, and behind a stockade fence. After recording a few more seconds of film, Bell, knowing his lunch hour was about over, walked back to the Post Office Annex. Before he resumed work, however, he went to an overlooking upper-story window of the annex and took some film of the School Book Depository and Dealey Plaza area, revealing a flurry of post-assassination activity. Bell did not speak with any police authorities and remained at his building until the end of his shift.

Bell never let authorities know that he was a witness or had movie film. His film did not receive any public notice until 1967, when a frame from it was reproduced in a *LIFE* magazine article about amateur photographers.

Charles Bronson, near the time of the assassination. *Courtesy Frances Bronson.*

Born in Illinois in 1918, Charles Leslie Bronson graduated from college in 1946 with a double major in chemistry and mathematics. In 1963 Bronson was chief engineer of Varel Manufacturing; he and his wife, Frances, lived in Dallas. In a later letter to his sisters, Bronson described November 22, 1963. "That morning at breakfast I told [Frances] of my plans that would see the fulfillment of a dream harbored since boyhood—getting to see the President of the United States and his Lady waving and smiling. The newspapers on Thursday evening had given a detailed map of the parade route and the timing of events from the moment the President landed until he was to depart."

Mr. and Mrs. Bronson traveled to Dealey Plaza and chose a location to view the motorcade: on top of a concrete pedestal, four and one-half feet high, located on the southwest corner of Main and Houston Streets. They had a sweeping view of the entire plaza area. The Bronsons had come well prepared to view and record the president's visit. Mrs. Bronson had brought a pair of binoculars, while Mr. Bronson had both a still and a movie camera.

Bronson's still camera was a classic of sorts, probably the oldest one used in the plaza that day. Purchased by mail order from Sears in May 1938, the chrome-trimmed, black-bodied 35mm Leica Model III-a, serial number 259903, had cost Bronson $169.95. The Leica camera was the first successfully marketed 35mm miniature camera manufactured, beginning in 1925, by Ernst Leitz Company in Germany. The III-a series was produced from 1935 to 1950. Bronson's camera had a 50mm f2.0 lens with serial number 379429. He had loaded it with daylight Kodachrome A transparency film with an ASA rating of 25 and had the shutter speed adjusted to 1/100 of a second.

Apparently the oldest camera in Dealey Plaza, this 1938 Leica Model III-a was one of two cameras used by Charles Bronson. After taking this picture, Bronson grabbed his movie camera in time to film the fatal shot. Reports about the Bronson pictures were declassified by the FBI in 1978. *Loaned courtesy of the Charles L. Bronson family.*

This photo of the Kennedy limousine on Elm Street corresponds to Zapruder frame 229, after Kennedy had already been wounded. *©1978 (Renewed 1996) Charles L. Bronson. All Rights Reserved.*

Testing his camera about six minutes before the president's arrival, Charles Bronson filmed nearly 8 seconds, which inadvertently included the Book Depository, with this Keystone Olympic K-35. Apparent movement in the sniper's window at a time when Lee Harvey Oswald may have been elsewhere could have meant Oswald's innocence. Urged in 1979 by the House Assassinations Committee to analyze the film, the Justice Department failed to do so. A private study for PBS/*Frontline* in 1993 determined that the movement was not human. *Loaned courtesy of the Charles L. Bronson family.*

Bronson also filmed the motorcade in Dealey Plaza and some of the assassination. This frame shows the proximity of the Secret Service car and bystanders to the presidential limousine at the moment of the fatal shot. *©1978 (Renewed 1996) Charles L. Bronson. All Rights Reserved.*

His movie camera was a new acquisition, having been purchased only a week or so earlier at a pawn shop on Elm Street in Dallas. The brown leatherette 8mm Keystone Olympic K-35 camera with serial number 774192 was mounted with a three-lens turret, including wide-angle and telephoto lenses. Bronson set the f-stop at f8 for bright sun. Though the normal speed for 8mm film was about 18 frames per second, Bronson set the speed at 12 frames per second to conserve film.

The first film sequence that Bronson took occurred before the motorcade arrived. Years later he recalled this scene: "Approximately six minutes before President Kennedy arrived in the Dealey Plaza area there was a commotion across from the School Book Depository building on Houston Street. An ambulance, with its lights flashing, arrived on the scene, and they evidently loaded someone in it that needed hospitalization. I thought I would capture that little bit of excitement. . . . I thought I had my telephoto lens in place, but instead I had my wide angle lens engaged. And that is the reason those frames that I shot of that ambulance and the commotion also included part of the School Book Depository building and also the window that Oswald is alleged to have fired the fatal shots from." The potential significance of this scene would not be brought to light until fifteen years after it was filmed.

About fifteen minutes after the Bronsons climbed onto the abutment, the motorcade could be seen traveling down Main Street toward their location. Bronson took a 5-second sequence with his movie camera, then switched to his Leica and made two pictures of the Kennedy vehicle as it came to the corner of Main and Houston Streets. He then switched back to the Keystone movie camera, taking a 7½-second film clip as the car moved along Houston Street.

> "I WAS WAITING TILL THE LIMOUSINE GOT INTO FULL VIEW . . . , BUT THE SHOT RANG OUT JUST BEFORE."
>
> *Charles Bronson*

At the Texas School Book Depository and now out of Bronson's view, the presidential automobile made a sharp left turn onto Elm Street. Meanwhile Bronson, with his Leica in hand, got ready to take a picture of the vehicle as it emerged into his view at his left. "I was waiting till the limousine got into full view . . . , but the shot rang out just before. I wasn't quite ready, but I had my finger on, and I had enough pressure on it so when the shot rang out . . . I instinctively jumped and snapped it at the same time." This picture exhibits quite a bit of detail concerning the triangular infield area between Elm and Main Streets. The president's limousine can be seen at the time when the assassination was in progress.

About five seconds after taking this Leica picture, Bronson grabbed his movie camera and filmed a brief, 2-second sequence. The Secret Service follow-up car is fully visible. Mrs. Kennedy is leaning over the president when suddenly a bullet hits him in the head, after which the first lady begins to rise from her seat. Bronson, peering through the small camera viewfinder, could not accurately see the action, but his ears were telling him something was wrong. As he related much later: "Then when the second and third shot rang out, that's when I decided they were rifle shots; and of course by that time people started running down there, and I told my wife, 'Let's get down from here. Those are rifle shots,' and a little chubby girl in a pink dress . . . came running across just before we got off of here and she said, 'Oh, my God, they shot the President!' Shortly after I got back to work did we learn that President Kennedy was dead and the Governor was critically wounded. . . . And the three loud shots still echoing in my ears and, yes indeed, the parade was over."

"... AND THE THREE LOUD SHOTS STILL ECHOING IN MY EARS, YES INDEED, THE PARADE WAS OVER."

Charles Bronson

On Sunday, November 24, Bronson dropped off his film and a note about its content to the local Kodak processing plant. Walter Bent, sales manager at the processing center, found Bronson's film and letter on Monday morning and telephoned the Dallas FBI. Agents contacted Bronson and viewed the film and slides that afternoon. The agents focused their interest on the assassination sequence, saying that they could not see anything there that was important. In an internal departmental memorandum, Agent Milton Newsom reported: "These films failed to show the building from which the shots were fired. Film did depict the President's car at the precise time the shots were fired, however, the pictures were not sufficiently clear for identification purposes."

As for Bronson and his pictures, that was the last contact he had with any investigative official. No agency contacted him again, no copies of his pictures were requested for study purposes, and the cursory examination of the film and slides by the FBI agents satisfied any interest in the Bronson eyewitnesses or the film and pictures. At the very least, the Bronson film complemented the films of Zapruder, Orville Nix, and Marie Muchmore while revealing a wider angle of view. (Although Marie Muchmore's film is available and important to the study of the assassination, it is not discussed here because neither she nor her camera has been located. More detailed information can be found in the author's *Pictures of the Pain.*) Most important, the agents had not noticed that in Bronson's first film sequence, the sixth-floor corner window of the Book Depository, the alleged assassin's perch, had also been filmed, about six minutes before the assassination. Bronson placed his original assassination films with the rest of his home movies and slides, every once in a while showing them to some friends and relatives.

By late 1977 Bronson's career had taken him to Oklahoma. Around that time documents relating to the Kennedy assassination from within FBI files were declassified and made available. One released document included the memo about the Bronson film. Earl Golz, a reporter for *The Dallas Morning News,* began looking for Bronson and his film. In November 1978, Golz went to visit Bronson in Oklahoma, taking with him Gary Mack, who had studied other photographs of the assassination. The two were very excited about Bronson's film, particularly noting the scene taken before the motorcade's arrival. Over 90 frames of this first sequence showed Houston Street before the assassination, with the sixth-floor corner window of the School Book Depository visible. It appeared to them that there might be discernible movement behind the sixth-floor windows.

With Bronson's permission, *The Dallas Morning News* commissioned the film technician and Warren Commission critic Robert Groden to make an enhancement study of the photographic materials. The November 26, 1978, edition of *The Dallas Morning News* broke the story about the Bronson film with a front-page headline declaring, "JFK Film May Reveal Two Gunmen." Groden was quoted: "There is no question that there is movement, and I am sure, given time and money, a computer could probably clarify the images a bit more."

Staff of the House Select Committee on Assassinations, which was investigating the Kennedy case at the time, became aware of the Bronson film. On December 2 a meeting was held at the Digital Image Processing Laboratory in Los Angeles, California. Arranged by staff of the Select Committee, the meeting included lawyers representing Bronson and ten photographic and digital image-processing experts. Several frames of the original film were viewed under a microscope, and one frame was scanned in color in a photo-digitizing system's microdensitometer. Among the conclusions sent to the Select Committee was that the experts "could not say conclusively whether or not the frame-to-frame changes in the sixth and fifth floor windows were due to real motion behind the windows." They unanimously disagreed with Groden's comment that "you can actually see one figure walking back and forth hurriedly." These experts added, "The apparent motion in the windows seems to be random, and therefore it is not likely to be due to human motion behind the window."

Time and money had run out for the House Select Committee. In its published report, the photographic panel, while pointing out that the apparent motion was not likely to have been caused by humans, also noted, "No firm conclusion could be reached without applying digital image processing." In its published report issued in 1979, the House Select Committee on Assassinations, under its recommendation for further investigations, neatly "passed the buck" by stating, "The

Department of Justice should contract for the examination of a film taken by Charles L. Bronson to determine its significance, if any, to the assassination of President Kennedy." Nothing, however, was ever done by the Justice Department or any other government agency to resolve the controversy over just what, if anything, was in that window.

Several times over the next fourteen years the Bronson film, scrupulously protected from copyright infringement by Bronson's lawyer, was the subject of several private, though not necessarily exhaustive, studies. All who knew about the film and its potential significance were shocked at the government's inattention to this matter.

Then in November 1993 the PBS investigative series *Frontline* aired a documentary on Lee Harvey Oswald. Among the background research done for the program was a scientific enhancement and analysis of that portion of the Bronson film showing possible movement in the suspect windows. According to the new study, however, when the color images were processed to reduce the grain noise, all these images appeared to be approximately the same. Analyst Robert Gonsalves concluded, in simple language, that no one could be seen walking about behind that window. Rather, "that's grain noise walking about."

The *Frontline* study may be the end of the controversy, but like so much else in the case, definitive answers have a way of becoming only more words with which to take sides. One of the most unsettling aspects of this matter of the Bronson film is the failure of the government to perform a comprehensive study on this important film.

. . . LIKE SO MUCH ELSE IN THE CASE, DEFINITIVE ANSWERS HAVE A WAY OF BECOMING ONLY MORE WORDS WITH WHICH TO TAKE SIDES.

Concerning the controversy over his film, Bronson told one researcher in 1985: "My personal opinion from what I've seen is that you can't see anything. As far away as that was in the film and the motion you had at the time, I don't think there is any way in the world you could get a definition of what was up there." In the final analysis, he may be correct. Charles Bronson died in 1995.

JACK DANIEL

Jack Daniel, from a family portrait made shortly before the assassination. *Courtesy Jack W. Daniel.*

Thirty-five-year-old Dallas resident Jack W. Daniel decided to take his three sons—Daniel, David, and Randy—downtown to see the president's motorcade. One son was celebrating his ninth birthday on November 22, 1963, and Daniel specifically picked a spot on the west side of the triple underpass, away from Dealey Plaza and the crowds. That way they had a better chance that the president would see them, and "he would be waving at my boys and not at the crowd." Daniel brought along his pistol-grip 8mm Argus movie camera, serial number 6117172, loaded with color film. He positioned himself several feet behind his boys so that they would be included in the foreground of his film as the president's car approached.

The view of the president's vehicle as it rushed through the underpass on its way to Stemmons Freeway and Parkland Hospital beyond was unexpected. Daniel would later comment that he had heard three shots and thought that something was wrong. The cars emerging from the underpass sped toward his position as two of the boys furiously attempted to get the president's attention. The 10 seconds of film made by Daniel include 176 frames that, when examined not in real time but in slow-motion and stop-action, show a confusing sight. The president's Lincoln, with fender flags flapping and alternating red lights flashing on the car's bumper, quickly approaches Daniel's position. The car has passed Dallas Police Chief Jesse Curry's lead car, which can be seen at the far right. There are three other cars and two motorcycles behind. Daniel pans right as the president's car passes parallel to him. All one can discern is a blurry vision, in the foreground, of the American flag on the right fender and a bulky image of agent Clint Hill on the trunk. Only later did the Daniel family learn that they had witnessed an assassinated president being taken to the hospital.

Standing alone behind his three sons on the west side of the triple underpass, Jack Daniel was unsure of what had happened. Daniel's movie film, made with this Argus Serial #6117172 camera with a pistol grip, shows the motorcade leaving the triple underpass before racing to Parkland Hospital. *Loaned courtesy of Jack W. Daniel.*

The Daniel film surfaced during the final days of the House Select Committee on Assassinations investigation in 1978. One of Daniel's sons, who at that time was living in Colorado, mentioned to a colleague his extraordinary ninth birthday outing to see the president and was urged to contact federal authorities about his father's film. Another son made the contact, and the House Select Committee called their father on December 28, 1978, stating an interest in the film. Daniel

The Kennedy motorcade emerges from the triple underpass about fifteen seconds after the assassination. Dallas Police Chief Jesse Curry's white car, which led the motorcade, falls behind the Kennedy limousine. *©1979 (Renewed 1992) Jack W. Daniel. All Rights Reserved.*

thereupon sent a copy of it to Washington. The film was used in an attempt to identify which Dallas police motorcycle officer might have been in the plaza and had his microphone stuck in the "on" position, causing the assassination to be transmitted and recorded by the police department. Officers B. J. Martin and James Chaney are the only cycle officers seen in Daniel's film.

MARY MOORMAN

Mary Ann Moorman, right, with friend Jean Hill in the press room of the Dallas County Sheriff's Office, not long after the assassination.
William Allen/Dallas Times Herald Collection, The Sixth Floor Museum.

One of the most familiar of the assassination photographs made at Dealey Plaza was taken with a Polaroid camera by a Dallas housewife. Of immense spot news importance, this photo was quickly copied and then distributed by United Press International (UPI) and Associated Press.

In 1963 Mary Ann Moorman was a thirty-one-year-old Dallas native married to a local plumber. Her close friend was Jean Lollis Hill, a thirty-two-year-old native of Ferguson, Oklahoma, who had moved to Dallas in August 1962. Since both women knew several of the officers taking part in President Kennedy's motorcade, they decided it would be fun to see the president and their officer friends and maybe get a picture of them in the procession.

The Polaroid camera Moorman had with her on November 22 was the result of the brilliant inventiveness of Edwin H. Land. Land had created a company that was in the forefront of polarized light usage and high-quality photographic work. In the area of popular photography, Land's idea of a self-contained camera and print developer for near-instant photography was first marketed in 1948. The camera's inner workings were nothing like those of the traditional camera. Two connected

This Polaroid Land 80-A camera is identical to the "instant" Polaroid camera used by Mary Moorman to photograph both President Kennedy and motorcycle officers known by her and her companion, Jean Hill. Three of the first four pictures were given to the officers and were eventually lost. The two surviving original pictures, like some other early Polaroid snapshots, have almost completely faded away.

film rolls were composed of a strip of a negative sheet on one roll and a strip of a positive sheet on another and included eight pods of a viscous development reagent. Once the exposure had been made, the photographer pulled the end of the film roll, at which time rollers pierced the foil envelope of the first chemical development pod. The film sheet was drawn between the chemicals. Cooked in the development solution for sixty seconds, the photograph was then removed from a rear film door. The photographer peeled the print away from its frame, thereby stopping further development.

Included in each box of Polaroid film was a glass vial containing a three-inch applicator with a sponge surface that had to be carefully and completely run across the just-developed picture. The applied coating of a polymer and acidic solution prevented further development and provided the image with a durable surface. If the procedure was not performed, the picture could lighten and fingerprints could mar the picture's surface. Regardless of the extra fuss required, the more than double cost of the Polaroid versus the traditional black-and-white prints, and the generally poorer quality of the snapshots produced, the camera and the system were an immense success. Twentieth-century Americans appreciated quick results.

Mary Moorman's Polaroid was known as the "Highlander," a Model 80-A series folding camera first put into production in 1954. Using Series 30 film, which made a picture in ten seconds, this camera produced eight 2¾-by-3½-inch prints. The camera had a 100mm focal lens and shutter speeds of 1/25 to 1/100 of a second. *Consumer Bulletin Annual* described the quality of the lens as "mediocre" and added, "The pictures obtained with this camera were about of the quality one would expect to obtain by use of an inexpensive box camera in the $6 to $15 price range."

Using Series 30 film, this camera produced a picture in ten seconds.

As the scheduled time for the motorcade neared, Moorman and Hill decided to take up a position on the south side of Elm Street near the curb and some 200 feet away from the southwest corner of the School Book Depository. The presidential automobile was preceded in the motorcade by several other vehicles, including a three-man advance motorcycle unit. Officer Glen McBride was a good friend of Moorman's from her high school days, and the first Polaroid photos she took were

Mary Moorman's last photograph, with the grassy knoll in the background, was taken about 1/6 of a second after the fatal shot. This digital restoration of the faded original was made by Larry Maver and the Itek Corporation in 1993.

of him astride his Harley-Davidson two-wheel motorcycle. Looming in the right background of the picture was the front of the Book Depository building, with most of the floors visible. All the Polaroid exposures except the last one were quickly peeled out of the camera and put into Hill's pocket.

Following the advance unit, the lead motorcycles of the escort came into view. These officers included W. George Lumpkin, who had known Moorman for many years and was aware that she took a picture of him. Moorman later indicated to a researcher that this photo did, on close examination, show the "assassin's window" in the Depository. After the assassination, Moorman recalled that neither she nor others ever saw anyone in any of the windows. Moorman gave Lumpkin the picture she had taken of him, though he eventually mislaid it.

The two young women were now caught up in the excitement as Chief Curry's lead car passed and was followed by that of President and Mrs. Kennedy traveling down Elm Street. Moorman did not snap her last exposure until after the president passed in front of her position. The vehicle was only some 20 feet to her left front when Moorman took her picture. At about that instant the two women heard shots and saw the violent reaction of the president and Mrs. Kennedy. As the car quickly sped off, Moorman and Hill fell to the ground to get out of harm's way. As the tail end of the motorcade passed in front of them and scores of spectators crossed to the north side of Elm and up the embankment, Hill followed suit, trying to locate someone she had seen, near the Texas School Book Depository, who seemed suspicious.

"... THEY WERE SHOOTING THINGS IN OUR FACES, AND HE WOULDN'T LET US OUT."

Jean Hill

After a short, fruitless look around the area of the railroad tracks, Hill realized that she "didn't want to be in on anything," and she returned to Elm Street. Moorman was standing at her original position but now was joined by a man. *Dallas Times Herald* court reporter James Featherston found Moorman with her camera and realized that she not only was a witness but also might have pictures. Moorman was crying, and Featherston had hold of her arm and possession of her camera, urging her to go with him. Hill rushed over, saying they had to leave. Featherston, realizing he had an important part of a breaking story, insisted the women go with him.

Hill recalled that Featherston practically ran them up to the corner of Main and Houston Streets. He took the women to the press room in the Sheriff's Office within the Dallas County Criminal Courts building. The atmosphere took on an excited and confused air as scores of people filled the press room. Apparently, Featherston and other members of the press had no intention of explaining the situation clearly to the women. Hill described Featherston's actions: "He kept standing in front of the door and he would let a camera in or someone to interview us and they were shooting things in our faces, and he wouldn't let us out." Though the women generally knew the difference between press interviews and investigators' questions, they apparently felt compelled to be cooperative with both. Nevertheless, they tired of answering the same questions over and over again.

> "My picture when I took it was at the same instant that the President was hit, and that does show in my picture . . ."
>
> *Mary Moorman*

At some point in the afternoon, members of the Sheriff's Office took brief statements and examined Moorman's pictures. Among interviews given by Moorman that afternoon was one conducted by ABC's Bill Lord. Moorman related: "My picture when I took it was at the same instant that the President was hit, and that does show in my picture . . . it shows the President he, uh, slumped. Jackie Kennedy was leaning towards him to see I guess. It all happened so suddenly, I don't think anyone realized, you know, what had happened." Asked about the shots, Moorman then stated: "There was three or four real close together, and it must have been the first one that shot him, 'cause that was the time I took the picture, and it was during that time after I took the picture, and the shots were still being fired, I decided I better get on the ground. . . . I was no more than fifteen foot [*sic*] from the car and in line of fire evidently."

The women later recalled that at the press room they allowed an examination of the pictures, which were out of Moorman's physical custody on several occasions. The assassination photo was quickly taken to the *Dallas Times Herald* offices, which shared a photo lab with UPI. It was copied there and then returned to Moorman at the Sheriff's Office. Hill remembered that as she and her friend gradually realized that the print had monetary value, they were disturbed not to know where the original was for periods of time. The news media did get possession of copies of Moorman's photo and published it, sometimes with and sometimes without Moorman's knowledge.

Among the millions of Polaroid prints to see the light of self-development, Moorman's Polaroid has turned out to be the most famous and most controversial one ever taken. Though the picture itself is all that a well-composed photograph should not be, once the viewer understands the time frame in which it was taken, its significance is revealed. None of the occupants' faces are in view. In the back seat Mrs. Kennedy is leaning to her right toward the president, who is obviously tipping unnaturally to his left. Only his full bushy hair and right shoulder are discernible. According to later studies, Moorman made this picture at about one-sixth of a second after the fatal head wound had occurred. Abraham Zapruder and Marilyn Sitzman are on top of a pedestal at the upper-right corner of the print, and the five-foot-high grassy knoll stockade fence and a concrete retaining wall are in view across the street from Moorman's position.

By the time Moorman left the Sheriff's Office in the early evening, the FBI had, with her permission, kept her picture of the president in the car. According to Secret Service Agent William Patterson, she surrendered to him "a Polaroid picture of the Texas School Book Depository" for use in the investigation, presumably a photo showing cycle officer McBride. At the request of local FBI agents, the picture was turned over to them within a day or two and was subsequently given back to Moorman.

Moorman was asked in 1964 to appear for a Warren Commission staff interview, but having recently twisted her ankle, she asked for a few days' delay, which was granted. She never heard from the commission again. Once published and released, neither the Warren Commission's *Report* nor the twenty-six volumes of hearings and evidence included any of Moorman's pictures.

Several eyewitnesses claimed to have noticed movements on the knoll at the time of the assassination. The Moorman picture, which included this area in the background, quickly became the subject for many researchers' magnifying glasses and conspiratorial theories. Given the Polaroid print's small size and its physical condition after development, this was not an ideal photograph. Couple those factors with the small area on the print taken up by the fence and tree line, together with the confusing texture of the tree line itself, and an investigation of this area by a photo interpreter is quite difficult. When various researchers studied this area of the picture, their observations could be as fanciful a search as that of a person making out animal forms among the clouds. In fact, even if there had been an assassin lurking in this area, identifying him as such would be quite difficult. Yet over the years more and more figures at different locations were seemingly being found by various researchers examining this same photo.

The Moorman picture, like so much else in the case, does not appear to give us simple, definitive answers. Many years later Mary Moorman noted of her photograph, "Something could have been there all this time and no one cared to do anything about it." Although some may wonder if "something" is indeed hidden away in her 24¢ print, what remains is a less-than-ideal piece of evidence.

ORVILLE NIX

Orville O. Nix, in a family snapshot from 1964.
Courtesy Gayle Nix Jackson and the Nix family.

The black spool of unprocessed movie film removed from the Keystone camera seemed indistinguishable from the dozens of other spools sent to a local photo lab for processing. It is unclear whether any film-processing technician noted the brief, dramatic event recorded within this particular movie and then made the authorities aware of its content. The shooter of this film, which included scenes of the assassination of President Kennedy, was Orville Orheal Nix Sr., a native Texan born in April 1911. In 1963 Nix lived in Dallas, was an air-conditioning engineer for the U.S. General Services Administration, was married, and had a grown son, Orville Jr.

After the processed film was returned to him and he realized its potential importance, Nix voluntarily turned the roll over to the FBI on December 1, 1963. Although desiring to be of assistance to the investigation, Nix emphasized that he wanted the film to be quickly returned to him. The Dallas FBI office made a copy, and the original was returned to Nix on December 4. The copy of the Nix film was forwarded to the FBI laboratory in Washington, where an additional copy was made.

The camera Nix had used on November 22 was a Keystone Auto-Zoom Model K-810 8mm movie camera. Manufactured by the Keystone Camera Company of Boston, Nix's model had a suggested retail price of just under $200. In the 1960s these built-in electric-eye cameras were becoming the most popular amateur movie cameras, allowing for self-adjustment to light sensitivity. The zoom or "infinity-variable-focal-length" lens was quickly replacing the older three-lens turret camera, though the complicated optics involved in a zoom lens made this type of camera much more expensive. Zoom lenses on the less-expensive side often produced

Orville Nix filmed the motorcade using this Keystone K-810 Auto-Zoom camera. He caught Nellie Connally , the wife of the governor of Texas, as she turned and said to President Kennedy, "You can't say Dallas doesn't love you." After the motorcade passed his original position on Houston Street, Nix ran to Main Street and filmed the motorcade, with the grassy knoll in the background, at the moment of the fatal shot. Incorrect settings caused much of his film to appear very dark. *Loaned courtesy of Orville O. Nix, Jr.*

poorer-quality pictures. *Consumer Bulletin* rated this Keystone series as an "intermediate" between their recommended and nonrecommended listings. The zoom lens had a 9mm to 27mm focal length, and the quality of the lens was rated as "fair" at normal and wide-angle settings but "poor" on the telephoto setting.

The color film used by Nix on November 22 was not a good choice. The Kodak Type A Tungsten film was designed for indoor use with photoflood light. If this film was to be used for daylight application, the photographer needed to use the camera's compensating Type A filter. Nix did not do this, and the ASA film speed rating for exposure control was 40 rather than 25. These factors produced film that was darker and grainier than the film that would have resulted if the correct outdoor film or correcting filter had been used.

Sometime around noon on November 22, 1963, Nix walked to Dealey Plaza and positioned himself near the northwest corner of Main and Houston Streets. As the presidential motorcade traveled down Main Street and turned right onto Houston, Nix began filming. His initial sequence of a little over 6 seconds recorded the president's limousine proceeding north on Houston Street away from Nix's position.

Figuring he might get a chance for another view across the grass infield toward Elm Street, onto which the motorcade was turning, Nix, according to an FBI report, "proceeded to a point about 20 feet west of Houston Street on the south side of Main Street and made the latter series across an open area which was in view of his position, using the zoom lens completely open." A later study would determine Nix to be at the south curb of Main Street approximately 200 feet from President Kennedy at the time when the president was shot in the head. His zoom lens covered approximately 75 feet of the grassy knoll area to the north of Elm Street.

This second film sequence lasted only slightly more than 6½ seconds. The presidential Lincoln enters the scene at camera right. The camera pans left, following the full length of the president's car as well as the following police cycles and the front portion of the follow-up car. At camera right a girl wearing a knee-length coat is observed running from the infield grass toward the car. At about frame #29 the

Seconds after the fatal shot, Secret Service agent Clint Hill reached Kennedy's car, jumped on the rear bumper, and climbed into the seat for the race to the hospital. *©1990 Nix Family. All Rights Reserved.*

girl stops dead in her tracks and thereafter leans hard back toward her right in a graphic recoil motion. The cause of her reaction is a gunshot, which hit the president's head at around frame #24.

Secret Service agent Clint Hill is seen running toward the president's vehicle. The outboard motorcycle closest to the camera overtakes the second cycle, which has abruptly stopped. Mrs. Kennedy rises from her seat, stretching out with her hand toward the trunk area, grabbing a piece of President Kennedy's head. On Nix's side of Elm Street, AP photographer James Altgens is seen in a picture-taking stance. Agent Hill manages to climb aboard the president's vehicle. The car picks up speed and races toward the triple underpass, beginning its rush to the hospital.

Seconds pass. Nix scurries 35 feet west on Main Street. He presses the camera shutter, and blurry frames of the street's pavement are quickly replaced by a view of Elm Street and the stairs leading up to the concrete pergola area. People are rushing across Main Street, and the area is being literally inundated by a mob of humanity. Part of the motorcade is still on the street. A blue Chevrolet convertible with cameramen aboard travels down Elm, followed by another convertible. This final filmed sequence lasts some 8 seconds.

In March 1966 in a filmed interview, Nix said he heard three shots during the assassination. At the time of the shooting he believed that all three shots had come from the fence area on top of the knoll, though he later accepted the conclusions of the Warren Commission. Both in Nix's film and in an examination of his filming locations, the Book Depository building was obscured to him, blotted out by the cement column of the north peristyle to the northeast. Except for two FBI reports that recorded only his film information, and despite his willingness to testify, Nix was never called or deposed by the Warren Commission or its staff. Critics of the Warren Commission contend that Nix's 1963 beliefs about the location of the shooter made him an unwelcome witness, one whom the commission therefore chose to ignore.

EXCEPT FOR TWO FBI REPORTS . . . AND DESPITE HIS WILLINGNESS TO TESTIFY, NIX WAS NEVER CALLED OR DEPOSED BY THE WARREN COMMISSION OR ITS STAFF.

Following the assassination, the news media scrambled for any possible visuals of the shooting scene itself. In early December Burt Reinhardt, of the UPI Newsfilm Division, was able to acquire from Nix his original film for $5,000, and on December 7 the UPI sent out to subscribers a sampling of frames from the Nix film. Fox-Movietone included the Nix assassination sequence in both full-frame and close-up format in a wrap-up newsreel about the weekend events, and two frames were reproduced in a 1964 souvenir hardcover book, *Four Days.*

In Washington during the early weeks of 1964, the newly established Warren

Commission staff was putting together its method of operations for investigating the case. The commission asked the FBI to study and establish the speed of the president's car, the distance traveled during the assassination, and the location of amateur filmmakers Nix and Zapruder during that time. FBI photographic expert Lyndal Shaneyfelt stated that this could be accomplished by examining the films and cameras involved, "accompanied by a survey of the actual site in Dallas." An FBI memorandum recommended obtaining Nix's camera for lab examination, followed by a study in Dallas of the site. FBI Director J. Edgar Hoover gave a less than enthusiastic approval of the study.

Contacted on January 29, "Mr. Nix advised the FBI was welcome to use the camera for experimental purposes and that he would be available as a witness if needed." After examining his camera, in early February the FBI laboratory reported that the average film speed of the camera was 18½ frames per second.

"Mr. Nix advised the FBI was welcome to use the camera for experimental purposes and he would be available as a witness if needed."

FBI, January 29, 1964

Beginning on January 29 and on at least three other days during as many months, Shaneyfelt and other FBI representatives met with staff of the commission and agents from the Secret Service. On these occasions they specifically examined the Nix film in concert with motion-picture films taken by Zapruder and Marie Muchmore. Following these meetings, on May 23 and 24, the FBI took primary responsibility in the survey reenactment of the assassination at Dealey Plaza.

Though Nix had provided his camera to FBI agents in early February, he had apparently assumed they would not need it for very long. Beginning in early March 1964, Nix made inquiries to the FBI about when he could expect it back, since his vacation time was approaching. Nix was told that if his camera was not available by the time he needed it, he could rent one, charging the cost to the commission.

By far the largest amount of paperwork about Nix had nothing to do with his witnessing the assassination but instead concerned his borrowed camera. Finally, on June 2, Nix's camera was personally delivered to him by Special Agent Robert Gemberling. That evening Nix called Gemberling at home and complained about the condition of the camera, including a missing take-up spool, loosened screws, and an inoperable footage indicator. Within a day Nix was instructed to take the camera to a local shop to put it "in first-rate working condition." The repair bill of $4.50 was paid by the local FBI office.

In 1965, assassination researcher Jones Harris studied pictures from the Nix film. The frames seemed to show that at the time of the assassination, a figure of what appeared to be a man was atop the grassy knoll. The figure seemed to be in a classic shooting position, standing behind and leaning on what looked to be a station wagon and taking aim with a rifle. His head, shoulders, and arms were all visible. Harris approached UPI Newsfilm Managing Editor Maurice W. Schonfeld and General Manager Burt Reinhardt, who had originally acquired the film from Nix. Realizing the importance of this potential find and the fact that, if it was borne out, the film's market value would be tremendous, the men cooperated in attempting to verify the existence of a gunman on the knoll.

Many assassination researchers saw these frames as important potential evidence. After some media notoriety about the possible grassy knoll gunman, a Massachusetts photo optics firm, Itek, agreed to do a photo study free of charge as a "public service." The Itek people did not slough off the image as easily refutable, and all involved appeared to be serious about finding out just what the figure was. The analysis was released in May 1967. Primary objectives of the study included identifying the shape of the "gunman" and "vehicle" and the line of sight to the area on Elm Street where President Kennedy received the fatal head wound.

Between Nix's filming of his two Elm Street sequences—at the time of the assassination and at a time moments later when the president's limousine had departed—Nix had moved about 18 feet to the left. This distance gave the Itek researchers a sufficient minimum separation to allow a stereoscopic analysis.

The study came up with interesting, though not startling, conclusions. The "assassin with a rifle" to the left of the concrete pergola "was found to be shadow and highlight details created by the sun casting shadows of tree branches on the wall of shelter 3." Stereoscopic study revealed that the shape did not possess a three-dimensional form, and improved imagery buttressed the conclusion that the shapes were patterns of shadows and highlights. If a shooter had been at this position, he would had to have been nine feet above the ground to get an unobstructed view of Elm Street, and his line of sight of the president would have been limited to less than 1/30 of a second before the fatal shot was fired.

A copyrighted UPI story regarding the Itek findings was released. Though this turned out to be a "non-story," the article's opening sentence gave it a broader interpretation. "An analysis by one of the nation's top photographic laboratories has demolished a widely circulated theory that a second gunman was involved in the assassination of President Kennedy." Itek and UPI had interpreted the entire grassy knoll area, which many had claimed to be the location from where shots were fired, as exclusively limited to the area in which Nix had filmed the "assassin with a rifle" shape. Contrary to the sweeping conclusion that no rifleman was present on the knoll, the study carefully examined only this narrow area close to the mystery image.

On January 17, 1972, Nix had a fatal heart attack. During the House Select

Committee on Assassinations investigation in 1978, the committee's photographic panel and its contractors examined the questions previously raised concerning the Nix film. Following several further examinations, the panel's conclusions basically agreed with those of the Itek study.

The panel also examined a feature that appeared to show movement left of the "rifleman" image in the dark shadow near the end of the retaining wall where the steps lead to the Elm Street sidewalk below. Some type of quick motion appears to take place there during the Nix film sequence. Several of these frames were scanned, with the data entered into a computer for enhancing the edges and sharpening the details. The resulting report stated, "The enhanced Nix film shows an object that can be construed as having a shape similar to that of a person." This apparent movement, as well as its possible significance to the assassination, remains an unresolved matter.

> "Let's find the truth and let it be known and let our lives go on."
>
> *Gayle Nix Jackson, 1991*

At the end of 1991 the assassination story experienced a renewed flurry of popular interest, predicated by the Oliver Stone movie *JFK*. Nix's granddaughter, Gayle Nix Jackson, appeared on several television programs at the time, telling of her grandfather's experience. Commenting on the idea that there might be something in this film that reveals a second gunman, she told one interviewer, "Let's find the truth and let it be known and let our lives go on." In 1992, before returning all copies of the film to the Nix family, the UPI could not locate the original film.

PATSY PASCHALL

Patsy Paschall, as she appeared at about the time of the assassination. *Courtesy Patsy Paschall.*

Patsy Paschall was a twenty-six-year-old court clerk who worked out of the "Old Red" Dallas County Courthouse on the corner of Houston and Main Streets in Dallas in 1963. Since the building in which she worked was on the route of the presidential motorcade on November 22, 1963, Paschall decided this would be a great opportunity to take movies of the event; she was especially interested in seeing First Lady Jacqueline Kennedy. On the morning of November 22, Paschall brought to work a newly purchased Bell & Howell Model 333 8mm movie camera loaded with color film. In the late morning she captured a view in the sky as *Air Force Two* and then *Air Force One* flew overhead on their approach to Love Field, carrying the vice-president and the president and their parties to Dallas.

. . . SHE WAS INTERESTED IN SEEING FIRST LADY JACQUELINE KENNEDY.

Stationing herself in an open window in a turret on the third floor on the Main Street side of the courthouse, Paschall could see up Main Street as the motorcade approached sometime after 12:20 P.M. She took several short segments of film of the motorcade including the two separate rows of Dallas police motorcycles preceding the cars, Police Chief Jesse Curry's white lead car, and then two views of the president and Mrs. Kennedy's convertible as it passed below. She stopped filming as the car began its turn onto Houston Street adjacent to Dealey Plaza. Remaining to watch from the window, several moments later Paschall heard an explosive noise followed, after a brief pause, by two additional bangs. "I was thinking that some fool was popping firecrackers." She became concerned when she saw people start falling to the ground.

Pointing her camera toward Elm Street, Paschall took a few seconds of film of the activity there and at the corner of Main and Houston Streets. In the background toward the triple underpass, one can see the president's car and the Secret Service follow-up car rushing into the shadows of the underpass and quickly gaining on Curry's lead car, which is veering to the left. Her view was unique due to its elevated position. From both upstairs at the third-floor window and downstairs at ground level, Paschall took several additional film clips of the frantic activity in the plaza following the assassination.

Her view was unique due to its elevated position.

A bit unnerved by the events and her recording of some of them, Paschall contacted a lawyer friend who, a few days thereafter, took the film to Dynacolor Corporation to have it processed. Told that any film of the assassination would be of interest to the FBI, the attorney, Fred Bruner, immediately contacted Agent

Patsy Paschall purchased this Bell & Howell Model 333 camera just to get pictures of Jackie Kennedy. She filmed *Air Force One* and *Two* flying overhead to Love Field with the presidential party, then captured a unique view of the motorcade passing below her as it reached Dealey Plaza. Later scenes show Kennedy's car entering the triple underpass, Abraham Zapruder leaving the area, and the crowd moving about on the grassy knoll. *Loaned courtesy of Patsy Paschall.*

About thirty seconds before the assassination, Patsy Paschall caught this unobstructed view down into the Kennedy limousine from the "Old Red" Dallas County Courthouse at Main and Houston. *©1996 Patsy Paschall. All Rights Reserved.*

Robert M. Barrett, who came over to the film lab. The agent asked to borrow the film for investigative purposes. Several weeks later the film was returned, along with a comment that it had no evidentiary value.

In 1967 the film was brought to the attention of *LIFE* magazine during its search for assassination-related pictures taken by amateurs. A frame from the film, together with a photograph and a brief interview with Paschall, was published in the November 24 issue of *LIFE*. In 1995 the film was again brought to public attention and became the subject of much media interest because it was thought that the film might contain new information.

BERT SHIPP

Bert Shipp, left, describing the scene at the Trade Mart to program director Jay Watson, before the official announcement of President Kennedy's death. *Courtesy WFAA-TV.*

Broadcast television debuted in the Dallas–Fort Worth area of Texas in September 1948. WFAA-TV, headquartered in Dallas, signed on late in 1949. The station was later owned, along with *The Dallas Morning News,* by the A. H. Belo Corporation and was affiliated nationally with the American Broadcasting Company (ABC). In 1963 WFAA, Channel 8, had the smallest news staff of the three major area television stations. News Director Robert Walker presided over an eight-man television news department, assisted by Chief Photographer Bert Shipp, who handled assignments. Walker's team was typically called on to take care of all aspects of a story including reporting and filming, as well as editing, writing, and voice-overs. Four radio-equipped mobile units and two remote trucks, including a 1961 vehicle holding six cameras and a 50-kilowatt portable generator, were on call for assignments.

Given the political importance of the presidential visit to Dallas, all the networks had made arrangements with their affiliates for late-afternoon film feeds to New York. Excerpts of President Kennedy's visit and his address at the Dallas Trade

As assistant news director and chief photographer of ABC affiliate WFAA-TV, Bert Shipp coordinated the station's film coverage. Waiting for Kennedy's arrival at the Trade Mart, Shipp was astonished when the president's car and several others raced by on their way to Parkland Hospital. After using this 16mm Bell & Howell DR to film there, Shipp returned to the studio and helped narrate film shot by other staff photographers. *Gift of Bert N. Shipp, WFAA-TV News.*

Mart would most likely be used during the nationally televised network evening news programs. The Texas visit, which had begun the day before, was a major story in the Lone Star State.

Along with live on-the-air local broadcasting, each station would also augment its coverage with news department photographers utilizing 16mm black-and-white Bell & Howell silent or Auricon sound cameras. These relatively lightweight cameras would photograph events and were able to film at a closer and more intimate vantage point than were the in-place, bulky television broadcast cameras. The resulting film would then be edited by the individual stations for rebroadcast locally and to the network. Such film would also be used in special recap programs planned by several of the stations for airing later Friday night, supplementing the live broadcasts, which could be videotaped.

The Dallas Trade Mart was the scheduled location for President Kennedy's luncheon address. Though the many members of the local and national press traveling along in the motorcade would report this newsworthy speech, other reporters and photographers were already at the Trade Mart, having previously staked out spots for good coverage. Bert N. Shipp, the energetic assistant news director and chief photographer for WFAA-TV, had arrived there early to take pick-up shots of the pre-arrival activities. With his spring-wound Bell & Howell DR 16mm camera equipped with a turret system of 1-inch, 2-inch, and wide-angle lenses, Shipp filmed exterior shots of a group of protesters, several carrying signs, including one reading "Hail Caesar." One clip shows a police officer directing several of the protesters across the street to keep them isolated from the arrival area. Shortly after 12:30, Shipp heard approaching sirens and decided to position himself by the main entrance to film President Kennedy's arrival. "As I saw the cars approach, I thought 'boy, they are going fast—they're going to miss the turn-off and have to backtrack.' It seemed strange that I couldn't see anybody in the car, just a foot sticking up in the air in the back of the President's

> "I SAW THE CARS APPROACH, I THOUGHT 'BOY THEY ARE GOING FAST—THEY'RE GOING TO MISS THE TURN-OFF AND HAVE TO BACKTRACK.'"
>
> *Bert Shipp*

From the Trade Mart, Bert Shipp filmed Kennedy's car and four others racing along Industrial (now Market Center) Boulevard to Parkland Hospital. *Courtesy WFAA-TV.*

"... It seemed strange that I couldn't see anybody in the car, just a foot sticking up in the air in the back of the President's limousine."

Bert Shipp

limousine." The foot Shipp saw belonged to Secret Service Agent Clint Hill. Realizing something was wrong, the cameraman managed to take a quick shot of the vehicles traveling up the incline in the distance.

Running to the back of the Trade Mart, Shipp found a police officer, who told him that the president had been "hit." He hitched a ride with another officer in an unmarked squad car to Parkland Hospital, leaving in the same small convoy as several homicide detectives. Approaching Parkland, Shipp immediately began filming. His clips include views of the motorcade cars parked helter-skelter in the entrance drive to the emergency room, Chief Curry, an obviously upset Senator Ralph Yarborough, Congressman Jim Wright, a view of the interior of the vice-president's convertible, several women White House staff members entering the emergency area, and the presidential Lincoln being fitted with its roof sections. While briefly inside the hospital attempting to find an open phone to call the station, Shipp asked an orderly in the hospital's blood bank about Kennedy's condition. The orderly stated, "He's gone."

After remaining at Parkland for some twenty minutes, Shipp, believing himself to be the only local cameraman at the scene, returned to the station to process and air his film. At 1:15 he briefly described, on-air, what he had seen and commented that his film would be quickly developed. At about 1:50 Shipp gave a running commentary as the first post-assassination film was broadcast unedited over Dallas television. The transmission was also picked up nationally by ABC. Shipp continued his career at WFAA-TV in Dallas and as of this writing is still with their news department.

THE TOWNERS

Jim Towner, from a portrait made in 1963.
Courtesy Patsy Towner Bailey.

Tina Towner, from film taken about two months before the assassination and located on the same reel as the Kennedy motorcade sequence.
Courtesy Tina Towner Barnes.

In 1963 Tina Towner was a typical thirteen-year-old who enjoyed the company of school girlfriends, was becoming interested in boys, and was not at all thrilled with junior high school. She lived with her parents in the Oak Cliff area of Dallas. Her dad, James M. Towner, was a civil engineer. When he learned of the impending visit of President Kennedy, he asked his wife and his youngest daughter, Tina, if they would like to go into town to see the excitement. Such a rare event was one not to be missed. Tina had little interest in politics, though she later recalled that when she learned that her father would allow her to miss school for the motorcade, "those were the magic words."

On November 22 Tina carried a note to school from her mother requesting that she be excused at ten o'clock. Though excited to be missing much of the school day, Tina was nervous about being questioned over the appropriateness of such an absence. She soon learned, however, that many other kids were getting out of school for the same purpose and that the school considered this event worthy of an excused absence. It was then that she realized that the president's visit was a really big deal, and she became caught up in her parents' excitement.

Jim Towner brought two cameras to record the event. He would use his Yashica 44 twin-lens reflex camera to take size 127 transparency slides of the motorcade. This Japanese camera had first been marketed in 1958, and Towner's gray-bodied

Towner, with his wife and his youngest daughter, arrived in Dealey Plaza more than an hour early to see the president. He chose the southwest corner of Elm and Houston to film with this Yashica 44 because the Kennedy limousine would be traveling slowly around the sharp turn. *Loaned courtesy of Tina Towner Barnes.*

model was mounted with a 60mm Yashinon lens. Its serial number was 166090732. Since Tina had some experience using the family's 8mm movie camera, her father let her handle taking the movies, thus getting Tina into the flow of the event by assigning her some responsibility. The camera was a Sears-brand Tower Varizoom 8mm movie camera, model number 584.91250. The f1.8, 9mm to 27mm lens was Japanese. Unfortunately, the meter that indicated the number of unexposed feet remaining in the movie camera was broken. Not knowing how much film was left on the spool, Towner cautioned his daughter not to waste film before the president's arrival.

Jim decided the best place to get a good view of the motorcade would be near its end. After picking his daughter up at school, he drove down and parked by the Union Railway Terminal. The family walked the four blocks to the southwest corner of Elm and Houston Streets, directly across from the Texas School Book Depository, arriving there at around eleven o'clock.

Now all they could do was wait. To a young, squirmy teenager with nothing to do, the waiting seemed interminable. Several times Jim directed his family's attention to all the people looking out of the windows of the buildings, including several in the Book Depository building, and commented on how these spectators had a real bird's-eye view. All three noticed the disturbance near the corner of Houston and Elm Streets when someone in the crowd collapsed from what they guessed to be a seizure or fainting spell. Shortly an ambulance, with sirens wailing, arrived, and it then quickly departed with the stricken spectator.

Finally, at about 12:30, the real excitement started. Tina and her parents heard the commotion growing to their right and rear as the police escort cars and motor-

The Kennedy limousine turns off Houston Street onto Elm, photographed by Jim Towner, with the Dal-Tex building in the background. *©1977 Tina Towner Barnes. All Rights Reserved.*

Barely a teenager, Tina Towner was most interested in getting out of school for a day, but she soon got caught up in the excitement of seeing the president and the first lady. The movie film she made with this Sears Tower Varizoom 584.91250 shows the Kennedys passing the front door of the Texas School Book Depository. Towner remembered that Jackie Kennedy looked right at her. *Loaned courtesy of Tina Towner Barnes.*

cycles turned onto Houston from Main Street. The Towners were now standing in the street several feet from the corner's long bending curb, which ran from Houston into Elm Street. Jim had seen that this position would give them a longer view than a position on a straightaway. Looking down into the camera viewfinder, Jim made a color transparency as the long, sleek presidential Lincoln began its wide turn. Following the movement of the car with his camera, Towner captured all six occupants in fairly good focus. The three men on the passenger side of the car were looking toward their right, with President Kennedy's full profile in view. Driver Greer, Mrs. Connally, and Mrs. Kennedy were looking to their left. Mrs. Kennedy was smiling and looking straight at the Towners. In the background loomed the Dal-Tex building, and at street level were over two dozen spectators, whose forms were horizontally misshapen due to Jim's panning his camera along with the movement of the car.

To her father's right and a half-step in front, Tina put the movie camera to her eye. As the limousine came into view from behind the crowd, she began filming.

> "WHAT I REMEMBER MOST WAS JACKIE KENNEDY'S BEAUTIFUL, BEAMING FACE . . . WHAT'S MORE, SHE WAS LOOKING AT— NO ONE ESLE, JUST ME."
>
> *Tina Towner*

"What I remember most was Jackie Kennedy's beautiful, beaming face. . . . What's more, she was looking at me—no one else, just me." Tina continued to pan left as the car traveled around the corner. Her film includes the front entrance of the building across the street with a sign over the entrance reading "Texas School Book Depository." Just after she stopped filming, Tina heard a loud report. She commented to no one in particular, "Some dummy is lighting fireworks!" Then there was another boom, and she looked around to see where they were coming from. "Finally, the third and last boom and, with that one, I turned to look at the School Book Depository building to see who was throwing fireworks out the window. I didn't see anything, though I was fairly sure that was where they were coming from."

Jim Towner had rushed a number of yards down Elm Street. Somewhere along the way he became aware that the noise was caused by a high-powered rifle. Now he

The Kennedy car passes in front of the Book Depository immediately below the window where the sniper's nest was found. Tina Towner's film is the only close-up of the president's limousine turning onto Elm. *©1983 Tina Towner Barnes. All Rights Reserved.*

took a picture of the activity farther down Elm Street. Towner's photograph shows the backs of three men in the foreground gazing down the street while farther down his side of the road a uniformed police officer is kneeling with his service revolver drawn. Closer to the underpass, police motorcycle officer Clyde Haygood is turning his cycle into the north curb of Elm Street, while closer to Towner's position, two press cars are in view. Moments later Towner walked further down Elm Street and took his third photo of the day showing activity in and around the knoll area.

Returning to his family, Towner told them that someone must have tried to shoot the president. Crowds were now gathering in clusters, and numerous police vehicles were arriving at the intersection of Elm and Houston Streets. Jim walked down to the opposite side of Elm Street, where one large cluster of people was gathered near the steps leading to the knoll area. Towner made his fourth photo, a picture of a trembling assassination witness, Charles F. Brehm, as he stood relating, almost incoherently, what he had moments earlier seen from his vantage point on the infield grass area. He was telling those around him that the president definitely had been hit by a bullet. Towner took a picture of Brehm and the numerous people around the witness, then returned to his wife and his daughter.

Tina took one additional film sequence some minutes after the shooting, panning right from the knoll area to the Texas School Book Depository. Unfortunately, when this sequence and her earlier film were developed, they were found to be somewhat underexposed, darker than normal. Tina, having experienced far more excitement and shock than she had bargained for, was beginning to feel nervous and shaky, and the three soon left the chaos behind. When they arrived at their car they turned the radio on for news. Only after they were back at home, as Mrs. Towner was making sandwiches for a late lunch, did they hear the official news that the president had been shot and had been declared dead.

Jim Towner later contacted *LIFE* magazine about his and his daughter's pictures, but they were not used until 1967. In *LIFE*'s issue containing an article on amateur photographers of the assassination, Jim's first and second photos were used, as were three frames of Tina's movie. The Towner family was not questioned, nor were their pictures examined, during the Warren Commission investigation.

The Towner family was not questioned, nor were their pictures examined, during the Warren Commission investigation.

PHIL WILLIS

Major Phil Willis, from a portrait made around 1963. *Courtesy the estate of Phil Willis.*

Like millions of other Americans in 1963, Phillip L. Willis was a self-styled amateur photographer who enjoyed taking pictures of family activities and special occasions. Thus, when he learned that President Kennedy would be visiting Dallas, Willis wanted to see and take pictures of this man whom he so admired.

Born in 1918 in Kaufman County, Texas, Willis as a young man had joined the Army Air Corps and in August 1941 was commissioned a second lieutenant. Willis was stationed at Bellows Field, Oahu, Hawaii, on December 7, 1941, when the Japanese attacked Pearl Harbor. Assigned to the 86th Observation Squadron, he managed to get his plane airborne during the first attack, though his plane was destroyed on the ground during the second attack. Later that day Willis assisted in the capture of the first Japanese prisoner of war when a Japanese miniature submarine washed ashore. Willis saw much action during the war, including flying fifty-two combat missions. He retired as a major in 1946, soon running for a seat in the Texas State House of Representatives and serving two terms representing Kaufman County.

By November 1963, Willis, his wife, Marilyn, and his two daughters, Rosemary (age ten) and Linda Kay (age fourteen), were living in Dallas. The morning of November 22, the Willises and Mrs. Willis' parents, Mr. and Mrs. William Stubblefield, decided they would all go to see the presidential motorcade. The two children were kept out of school for the event.

When Willis left the house that morning he took with him his Argus 35mm Autronic I, Model 35156-M camera with an f2.8 Cintar lens. Purchased in June 1962 at a military post exchange in San Antonio, the camera had three settings: "flash,"

With his entire family present, Phil Willis used this Argus 35mm Autronic I Model 35156-M to shoot 27 color slides before, during, and after the assassination—more than any other photographer. On his way to get his film developed at Kodak's processing plant, near Love Field, Willis made one last picture—of *Air Force One* returning to Washington with the body of President Kennedy.
Loaned by the estate of Phil Willis.

"scene" (for still photos), and "action" (for moving shots). It was loaded with Kodachrome color slide film with an ASA rating of 25.

Employed as an executive car salesman, Willis met his family at about noon and let a co-worker drop them off near the corner of Main and Houston Streets. "I figured that would be the ideal spot. I wanted them to see the President and get some pictures. I had no idea what I was getting into." The children remained with their father, while Mrs. Willis and her parents opted to move down to the colonnade area on the west side of Houston Street.

> ". . . I WANTED THEM TO SEE THE PRESIDENT AND GET SOME PICTURES. I HAD NO IDEA WHAT I WAS GETTING INTO."
>
> *Phil Willis*

At about 12:28 P.M., the approaching motorcade could be seen on Main Street. After taking several photos of the lead vehicles, Willis snapped a picture as the presidential vehicle neared the corner of Main and Houston Streets. He then immediately moved onto the Houston Street sidewalk, scurrying some 60 feet north. In his fourth slide, Willis captured the limousine as it finished its turn onto Houston Street. Whether by chance or design, this picture includes, on the extreme right side, the vice-presidential convertible, with Lyndon Johnson in the back seat, and is thus the last identifiable photograph showing the thirty-fifth president and his vice-president in the same picture.

Moving about 40 feet up Houston Street, Willis took a fifth picture as the limousine passed his position. Willis later recalled, "Then, I immediately ran across the Plaza, raced over to Elm Street and stationed myself on the curb in front of the Texas School Book Depository." With his children following behind, Willis traveled the 120 feet in time to snap a blurry photo of the passengers in the limousine, only some 15 feet from his position.

The most important of Willis' slides was his seventh in the sequence. Later, government research timed this photograph as having been taken at the same time as Zapruder frame 202. Less than three seconds after his sixth picture, Willis had moved slightly down Elm toward the departing presidential vehicle. He raised his camera to his eye. He later remembered: "As I was about to squeeze my shutter, that is when the first shot rang out and my reflex just took that picture at that moment.

Taken as a reaction to the first shot, this picture shows President Kennedy, below the arrow, and Abraham Zapruder, above and to the right of the Stemmons Freeway sign.

> "As I was about to squeeze my shutter, that is when the first shot rang out and my reflex just took that picture at that momemt."
>
> *Phil Willis*

I might have waited another full second . . . but being with my war nerves anyway—when that shot rang out, I just flinched and got it." From his military and hunting experience, he knew that the sound was a shot from a high-powered rifle and that the bullet had hit.

This photograph would have been a very disappointing slide under normal circumstances. The president's car is not the prominent feature, and only the backs of the heads of the Kennedys and the Connallys can be glimpsed. Instead, the bulky Secret Service follow-up car and two motorcycles on the left are the prominent features of this slightly blurred picture. The action on the street has obviously passed Willis by. Yet this picture captures the scene at the time the president was being fired upon. This slide would be the subject of much later examination and study. After Willis took this picture, events moved quickly. He remembered exclaiming about the president, "Someone is shooting at him!" He also remembered hearing two additional shots being fired at about two-second intervals. Willis later stated: "They did not ring out long like a bullet shot that is fired into mid-air in a distance. I knew it hit something, and it couldn't have been a firecracker or anything like that." Willis' two daughters had been running alongside the presidential limousine; fearing for their safety, their father yelled for them to come back. The girls had stopped in their tracks during the shots and had headed back to their mother.

Willis remembered that after the shots, he screamed for someone to "ring the building," meaning the Texas School Book Depository, since he was sure that this was where the shots had come from. Approximately half a minute after the president had received his fatal head wound, Willis took an eighth photograph from a position farther down Elm Street. This photo shows over half a dozen men on the south side of Elm Street running in the direction of the triple underpass. The VIP vehicles had already sped off, en route to Parkland Hospital, and motorcycle policeman Clyde A. Haygood had parked his cycle by the north curb of Elm Street and can be seen running up the incline toward the overpass. A portion of the motorcade seems to have stalled in the road, with a passenger on the driver's side of a station wagon opening the door and getting out. Seconds later, and still farther down the street, Willis took a ninth photograph of the Elm Street scene. At about this point Willis rejoined his family, his daughter Rosemary telling him, "Oh, Daddy, they have shot our President!"

Since Willis believed that the gunfire had originated from the Book Depository building, he went up to that area and began taking pictures of police activities near the front of the building. The family remained in this vicinity for the next hour, with Willis taking some fifteen additional photographs. The girls were very much upset, and at one point Willis ended up lying "down on the ground and vomiting due to . . . old war ulcers." The Willis family drove to the Kodak processing laboratory near Love Field. Within half an hour, his film was developed. According to Willis, "We viewed them for the first time and went home after dark—very sick." The Willises spent the rest of the weekend in their home, keenly viewing the television coverage around the clock. The following Monday, Willis loaned his slides to the Secret Service. They were returned to him in January 1964.

"WE VIEWED THEM FOR THE FIRST TIME AND WENT HOME AFTER DARK—VERY SICK."

Phil Willis

Finding that few pictures of the assassination scene were available, Willis decided to market twelve of his best slides, feeling "compelled to make them available to the public." A two-page description of the slides was included with the package.

Like several other photographers, Willis was not interviewed by government investigators, who also did not show much interest in his photographs, until it was evident that publicity concerning them was being generated. In June 1964, seven months after the assassination, Willis and his wife were interviewed by an FBI agent. On July 22, 1964, Willis and his daughter Linda Kay gave testimony in Dallas to a Warren Commission staff attorney.

Both Phil and Marilyn Willis were subpoenaed and gave testimony during the Clay Shaw trial in New Orleans in 1969, and they were interviewed in Washington, D.C., by a staff member of the House Select Committee on Assassinations in 1978. Their daughter Rosemary, sixteen years after the event, confirmed that she had heard three shots during the assassination, shots that had come from the direction of the Book Depository building. She added, however, that she believed that Oswald had been at the window on purpose, so that people would believe he was the assassin. She believed that other shots, particularly the one that hit the president in the head, had been fired from elsewhere, possibly with a silencer.

After viewing the Zapruder film numerous times and reflecting on the events, Phil Willis in the 1980s told one researcher: "I don't care what any experts say. They're full of baloney. I've shot too many deer. I've hit a deer in the head and his horns fly 20 feet with the direction of the bullet. No one will ever convince us that the last shot did not come from the right front, from the knoll area."

Willis died in Dallas in January 1995. During his lifetime, Phil Willis was at two of his country's defining moments, the attack on Pearl Harbor and the assassination of President Kennedy.

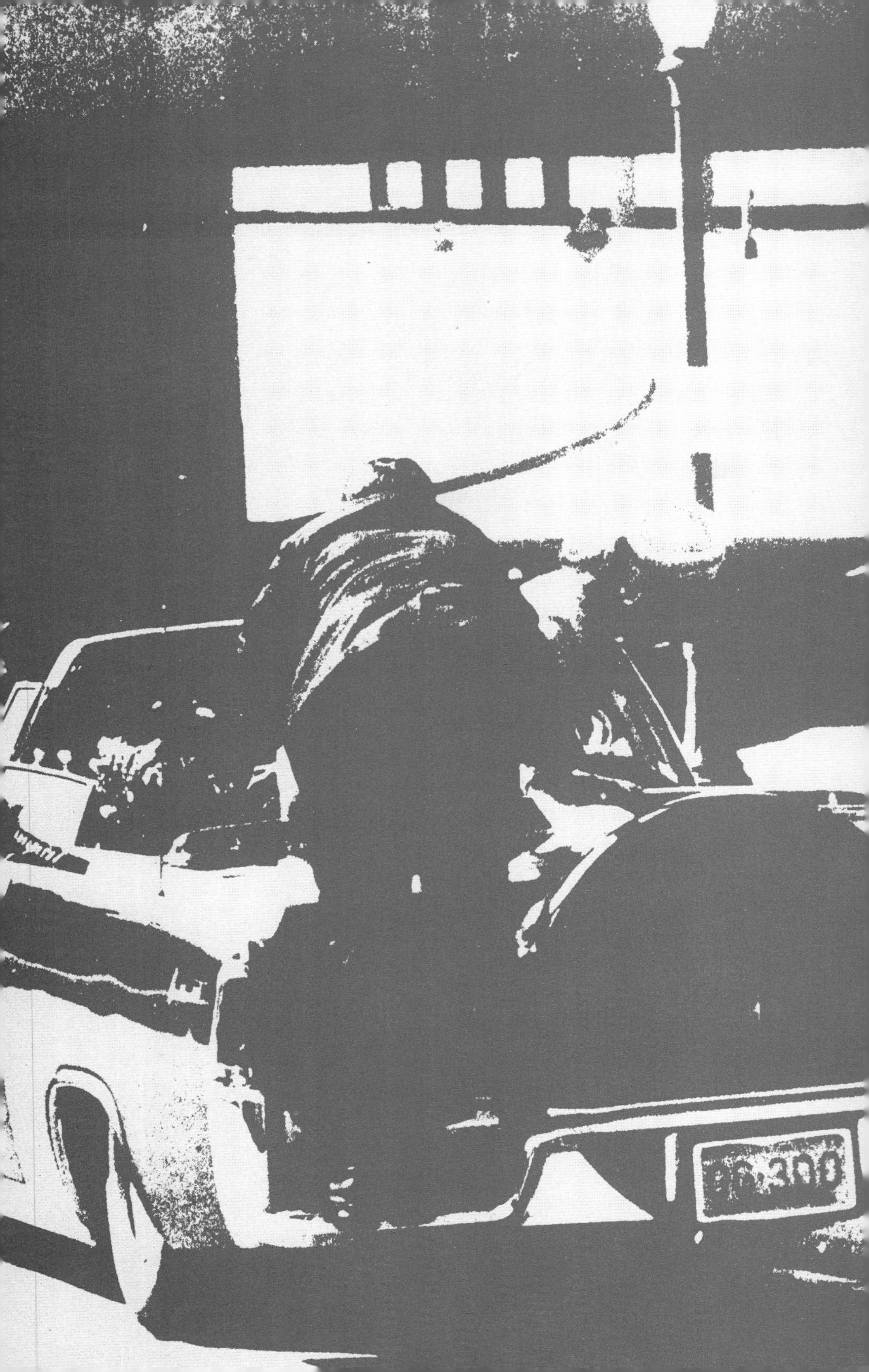
300

CONCLUSION

Thus these twelve photographers from Dallas captured important images of the crime story. Their cameras, included in the special Sixth Floor Museum exhibit, serve as testimony to the differences in cameras used in 1963 and to how fortunate we are to have these images, made in large part by amateur photographers. Of the thirteen cameras on display, only two were used by professionals.

In 1963, most of these cameras were the latest, most modern means for making pictures. By today's standards, of course, many are antiquated and almost quaint. The Polaroid was one of the first to give "instant pictures"; the Shipp camera was the type being used in the television industry; and the Zapruder camera was typical of what American fathers were buying to record their growing families. All but the Shipp camera were used in Dealey Plaza.

The Kennedy assassination images that remain fixed in the minds of Americans were made from the cameras on display here. The unforgettable photographs of a young president slumping over and his horrified first lady climbing out on the trunk of the limousine were the basis for vivid, emotional memories. All of the amateur photographers came out to Dealey Plaza that day simply to take pictures to have as their personal souvenirs of President and Mrs. Kennedy's visit to Dallas. In the end they recorded history. Their camera work, along with that of the other photographers on the scene, has preserved and given to us the closest thing to a time machine that we shall ever have, allowing us to "view" part of the reality of Dealey Plaza on November 22, 1963, when the thirty-fifth president of the United States was cruelly and obscenely cut down by assassination.

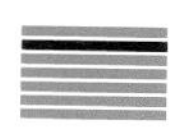

Opposite page: Adapted from a James Altgens photo showing Mrs. Kennedy on the trunk seconds after the final shot. *Courtesy, AP/Wide World Photos.*

STAFF OF THE SIXTH FLOOR MUSEUM INVOLVED WITH THIS PUBLICATION

Jeff West, Executive Director
Marian Ann J. Montgomery, Ph.D., Director of Interpretation
Gary Mack, Archivist

Other staff as of November 1, 1996: Elathon Anthony, Janice Babineaux, James Bagby, Donnell Banks, Kevin Berry, Megan Bryant, Sonia Cervantes, Larissa Church, Jennifer Cohen, Dean Espinoza, Tina Garcia, Ronald Gonzales, Pedro Gonzalez, Anthony Harris, Sue Hilty, Christina Jasso, David Kilbourn, Bertrand Lamb, Ruthie Lawson, Mia Llarena, Jewel Marshall, Nicklous Nelson, Richard Oats, Eric Oglesby, Robert Porter, Fabian Solorio, Dora Soto, Timothy Tazelaar, Aaron Thomas, Thomas Thompson, Raymond Weaver, Karen Wiley, Bryce Williams, Sanford Williams and Stacy Young.

For additional information about The Sixth Floor Museum's exhibitions, publications, educational programs or contribution opportunities, please contact:

THE SIXTH FLOOR MUSEUM
411 Elm Street, Suite 120
Dallas, Texas 75202-3301
(214)653-6659
FAX (214)653-6657

http://www.jfk.org